T O P I C S   I N   M  S

Hyperbolic Functions

V. G. Shervatov

Translated and adapted from the second Russian edition (1958) by

A. GORDON FOSTER *and* COLEY MILLS, JR.

SURVEY OF

RECENT EAST EUROPEAN MATHEMATICAL LITERATURE

A project conducted by

ALFRED L. PUTNAM *and* IZAAK WIRSZUP

Department of Mathematics,
The University of Chicago, under a
grant from the National Science Foundation

D. C. H E A T H   A N D   C O M P A N Y   B O S T O N

Library of Congress Catalog Card Number: 61-17846

PREFACE TO THE AMERICAN EDITION

IN THIS BOOKLET the hyperbolic sine, hyperbolic cosine, and hyperbolic tangent are introduced in connection with the geometric properties of the hyperbola, and the fundamental properties of these functions are derived. Natural logarithms are then discussed.

With the aid of complex numbers, basic formulas are derived which interrelate hyperbolic functions, trigonometric functions, and the number e. Finally, infinite series expansions of $\sinh t$, $\cosh t$, $\sin t$, $\cos t$, and e^a are given.

Two years of high school algebra and an acquaintance with trigonometry are sufficient to enable the reader to understand Chapters 1 and 2. To understand fully the last chapter it is necessary to have some acquaintance with the theory of limits. However, those who do not possess this background will be able to follow much of the discussion.

CONTENTS

CONTENTS

Hyperbolic Functions

1. The Hyperbolic Rotation

1. HOMOTHETIC TRANSFORMATIONS

In solving problems in geometry we often use the following type of transformation. Pick a point O in the plane and a positive number k. If A is any other point, let us transform the point A into the point A' such that A' lies on the half-line OA and $\dfrac{OA'}{OA} = k$ (Fig. 1a, b).

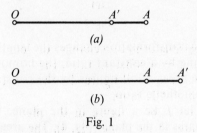

(a)

(b)

Fig. 1

We leave the point O fixed by the transformation. Such a transformation is called a *homothetic transformation*, O is called the *homothetic center* (or *center of similitude*), and k is called the *homothetic ratio* (or *ratio of similitude*). Obviously, if $k < 1$, then $OA' < OA$ (Fig. 1a), while if $k > 1$, then $OA' > OA$ (Fig. 1b).

Under a homothetic transformation every figure F is transformed into a figure F', similar to F (Fig. 2). If $k < 1$, F' is smaller than F, while if $k > 1$, F' is larger than F.

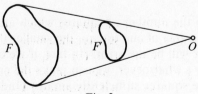

Fig. 2

1

A homothetic transformation transforms a straight line into a straight line (Fig. 3a), parallel lines into parallel lines (Fig. 3b), and circles into circles (Fig. 3c).

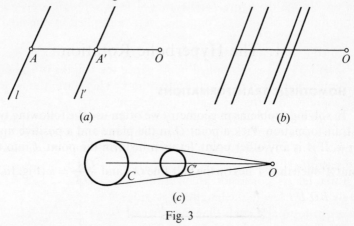

(a)

(b)

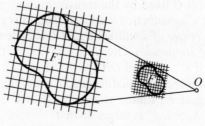

(c)

Fig. 3

A homothetic transformation changes the lengths of all line segments in the plane by a constant ratio, the homothetic ratio k. It also changes the areas of all figures by the constant ratio k^2, the square of the homothetic ratio.

To see this, let F be a figure in the plane. Consider also a grid of small squares in the plane (Fig. 4). The area of F is approxi-

Fig. 4

mately equal to the number of squares which are contained in F multiplied by the area of one square; the smaller the squares of the grid, the smaller will be the error. (In fact, if we choose any small positive number ε whatsoever, we can make the error smaller than ε by making the squares sufficiently small.) Under a homothetic transformation the grid of squares is transformed into a new grid of squares and the figure F into the figure F', which will contain exactly as many squares of the new grid (the squares will be smaller if $k < 1$ and larger if $k > 1$) as there were squares of the first grid inside the figure F. The area of F' is approximately equal to the number of squares contained in it multiplied by the area of one square.[1]

But the area of each new square is equal to the area of one of the original squares multiplied by k^2, since the lengths of the sides of the original squares are multiplied by k. Therefore, the area of F' is equal to the area of F multiplied by k^2.

As an example of the application of homothetic transformations, let us solve the following problem: *Inscribe in a given right triangle ABC a rectangle BDEF so that the lengths of its sides are in a given ratio* (Fig. 5).

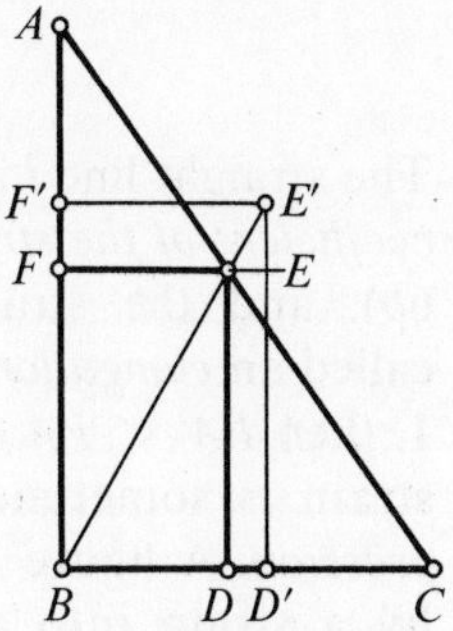

First let us construct an arbitrary rectangle $BD'E'F'$, with the lengths of its sides in the given ratio and such that the vertices D' and F' lie respectively on the sides BC and AB of the given triangle. Let E be the point of intersection of the line BE' and the side AC of the triangle. It is easy to show that the homothetic transformation with B as the homothetic center and

$$k = \frac{BE}{BE'}$$

Fig. 5

as the homothetic ratio will transform the rectangle $BD'E'F'$ into the required rectangle $BDEF$. From this we can easily construct the desired rectangle. When the given triangle ABC is not a right triangle, the problem can be solved in an analogous way. We shall not dwell on this here.

2. STRAINS

We shall need to use another transformation called a *strain*. Let l be a straight line in the plane. Let us transform the point A in the plane into the point A' such that A' lies on the perpendicular PA

---

[1] A rigorous argument would be more complex than this, since it would involve using a limiting process.

dropped from A to l and $\dfrac{PA'}{PA} = k$, some positive constant (Fig. 6a, b). Every point of the line l is left fixed by the transformation.

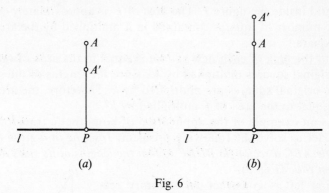

Fig. 6

The straight line l is called the *axis of the strain,* and k is called the *coefficient of the strain.* If k is greater than 1, then $PA' > PA$ (Fig. 6b), and the strain is sometimes called an *elongation.* If k is less than 1, then $PA' < PA$ (Fig. 6a), and the strain is sometimes called a *compression.* A figure F is transformed by a strain into a new figure F', which is usually *not* similar to F. In Fig. 7, $k = \dfrac{1}{3}$; that is,

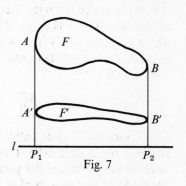

Fig. 7

$$\frac{P_1 A'}{P_1 A} = \frac{P_2 B'}{P_2 B} = \cdots = \frac{1}{3}.$$

Several properties of strains are analogous to the properties of homothetic transformations.

(a) *A straight line is transformed by a strain into a straight line.*

Suppose that a strain has axis l and coefficient k; let m be any straight line. If m is parallel to l and at a distance d from l, then m is transformed into a straight line m' parallel to l and at a distance kd from l (Fig. 8a). On the other hand, suppose that m and l intersect, say at the point O (Fig. 8b). Under the strain the point O remains fixed. Let A be any point different from O on the line m, and let A' be the point into which A is transformed by the strain. Then $PA' = k \cdot PA$. Let B be another point on the straight line m. Let

4

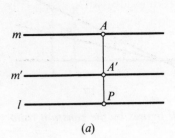 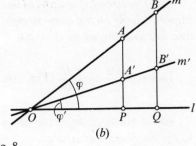

(a)   (b)

Fig. 8

B' be the point where the perpendicular BQ from B to l intersects the straight line OA'. The triangles OQB and OPA are similar, and the triangles OQB' and OPA' are similar; hence,

$$\frac{QB'}{QB} = \frac{PA'}{PA} = k,$$

that is, $QB' = k \cdot QB$. From this last equality we see that the strain transforms the point B into the point B'. Since B was an arbitrary point of the line m, this line is transformed by the strain into the line OA', which we shall call m'.

(b) *Parallel lines are transformed by a strain into parallel lines.*

Let the lines m and n be parallel; then they have no point of intersection. In that case the lines m' and n' into which m and n are transformed also have no point of intersection (since a point common to m' and n' could only result from a point common to the lines m and n); this shows that the lines m' and n' are also parallel (Fig. 9). Note that if φ and φ' are the angles formed by the original line m and the image line m' with

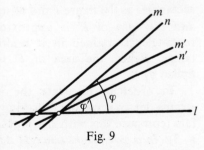

Fig. 9

the axis of the strain l, then from Fig. 8b it is easy to see that

$$\tan \varphi' = \frac{PA'}{PO} = \frac{k \cdot PA}{PO} = k \cdot \frac{PA}{PO} = k \cdot \tan \varphi.$$

Hence, it also follows from this that parallel lines (intersecting l with the same angle φ) are transformed into parallel lines (intersecting l with the same angle φ').

(c) *The ratios of lengths of line segments lying on the same straight line are unchanged by a strain.*

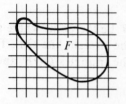

Indeed, $\dfrac{AB}{BC} = \dfrac{A'B'}{B'C'}$ (Fig. 10).

Fig. 10

(d) *A strain changes the areas of all figures by the constant ratio k, the coefficient of strain.*

To see this, let F be a figure in the plane. Consider also a grid of small squares whose sides are parallel and perpendicular to the axis of the strain. The area of F is approximately equal to the number of squares which are contained in F multiplied by the area of one square (Fig. 11). The squares are transformed by the strain into a grid of rectangles, the area of each of which is the area of one of the original squares multiplied by k (one of the dimensions of the square is unchanged, while the other is multiplied by k). The figure F' contains exactly the same number of rectangles as the figure F did of squares, and the area of F' is approximately equal to the number of rectangles contained in it multiplied by the area of one rectangle. Hence, the area of F' is equal to the area of F multiplied by k.

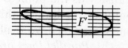

Fig. 11

In order to illustrate the use of strains, let us solve the following problem (compare this with the problem on p. 3): *In a given right triangle ABC inscribe a rectangle $BDEF$ of given area T* (Fig. 12). For the solution, apply a strain with axis BC and coefficient

$$k = \frac{BC}{BA}$$

to the triangle ABC. This strain trans-

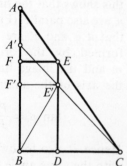

Fig. 12

6

forms the triangle ABC into an isosceles right triangle $A'BC$. Since

$$BA' = k \cdot BA = \frac{BC}{BA} \cdot BA = BC,$$

the area of the triangle $A'BC$ is kS, where S is the area of the triangle ABC. By property (d), any rectangle $BDEF$ of area T inscribed in ABC would be transformed into a rectangle $BDE'F'$ with area kT. Therefore, in the isosceles right triangle $A'BC$ let us inscribe a rectangle $BDE'F'$ of area kT.

It is easy to do this, for

$$S_{BDE'F'} = S_{\triangle A'BC} - (S_{\triangle E'DC} + S_{\triangle A'F'E'});$$

therefore, $\quad S_{\triangle E'DC} + S_{\triangle A'F'E'} = S_{\triangle A'BC} - S_{BDE'F'} = kS - kT.$

On the other hand,

$$S_{\triangle E'DC} + S_{\triangle A'F'E'} = \frac{1}{2}DE'^2 + \frac{1}{2}F'E'^2 = \frac{1}{2}(DE'^2 + F'E'^2) = \frac{1}{2}BE'^2.$$

(Here we make use of the fact that the triangle $A'BC$, and consequently the similar triangles $E'DC$ and $A'F'E'$, are isosceles.) Thus, we obtain

$$\frac{1}{2}BE'^2 = kS - kT.$$

Now that we know the length of the segment BE', we can at once find the point E'. After that we can construct the rectangle $BDE'F'$ inscribed in the triangle $A'BC$, and finally the rectangle $BDEF$ inscribed in the triangle ABC.

Depending on the value of T, the problem may have two, one, or no solutions. When the given triangle ABC is not a right triangle, the problem can be solved in an analogous way, but we shall not consider this here. A geometric solution of this problem without using strains is unknown.

As contrasted with homothetic transformations, strains do not transform circles into circles. A circle is transformed by a strain into a curve called an *ellipse* (Fig. 13). With properties (a) — (d), we could use strains to study a number of geometric properties of the ellipse, but such a study would be beyond the scope of this booklet.

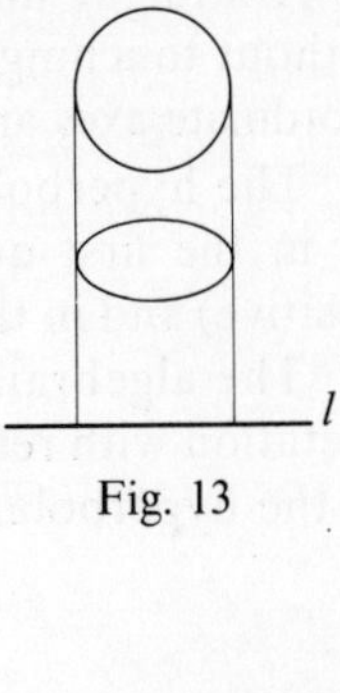

Fig. 13

7

3. THE HYPERBOLA

In the following sections an important part will be played by the graph of the curve whose equation is

$$y = \frac{a}{x} \quad \text{or} \quad xy = a \qquad\qquad (a \neq 0).$$

This curve is called a *hyperbola* (Fig. 14).

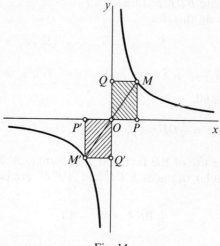

Fig. 14

It is obvious that the greater the absolute value of x, the smaller will be the absolute value of y, and conversely. Symbolically, if $x \longrightarrow \infty$, then $y \longrightarrow 0$, and if $y \longrightarrow \infty$, then $x \longrightarrow 0$. Geometrically, this means that the hyperbola comes arbitrarily close to the coordinate axes but does not actually intersect them, for it follows from the equation $xy = a$ that neither x nor y can be zero.

A straight line which a curve approaches nearer and nearer without touching it is called an *asymptote* of that curve. Thus, the coordinate axes are asymptotes of the hyperbola.

The hyperbola is composed of two *branches,* which for $a > 0$ lie in the first quadrant of the coordinate system (x and y both positive) and in the third quadrant (x and y both negative).

The algebraic equation $xy = a$ has a simple geometric interpretation with reference to the hyperbola. If M is an arbitrary point of the hyperbola, then the area of the rectangle $MQOP$, which is bounded by the coordinate axes and the two straight lines through M and parallel to the axes (Fig. 14), is equal to a. In other words, the area of such a rectangle is independent of our choice of the point M. That is, since $OP = x$ and $PM = y$, we have

$$S_{MQOP} = OP \cdot PM = x \cdot y = a.$$

Calling the rectangle $MQOP$ the *coordinate rectangle of the point M*, we can say that *the hyperbola is the locus of those points lying in the first and third quadrants of the coordinate system whose coordinate rectangles have a given area.*

The hyperbola has a *center of symmetry*: the two branches of the hyperbola are symmetric with respect to the origin O of the coordinate system. (The coordinate rectangles $MQOP$ and $M'Q'OP'$ symmetric with respect to O (Fig. 14) have equal areas.) The hyperbola also has two *axes of symmetry*, the lines aa and bb which bisect angles between the coordinate axes (Fig. 15). In fact, the

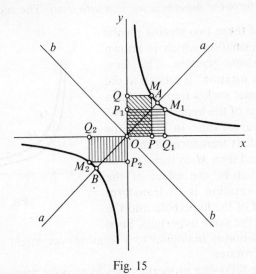

Fig. 15

coordinate rectangles $MQOP$ and $M_1Q_1OP_1$ (symmetric with respect to aa) have equal areas; similarly, the coordinate rectangles $MQOP$ and $M_2Q_2OP_2$ (symmetric with respect to bb) have equal areas. The center of symmetry O and the axes of symmetry aa and bb are usually simply called the *center* and the *axes* of the hyperbola; the points A and B in which the hyperbola intersects the axis aa are called the *vertices* of the hyperbola.

4. THE HYPERBOLIC ROTATION

Consider the hyperbola $xy = a$, and apply a strain with axis the x-axis and with coefficient k. Under this transformation the hyperbola $xy = a$ is transformed into the hyperbola $xy = ka$: the abscissa x of every point remains unchanged, while the ordinate y is changed to ky (Fig. 16). Now let us apply another strain—this time with axis the y-axis and with coefficient $\frac{1}{k}$. Under this transformation the hyperbola $xy = ka$ is transformed into the hyperbola $xy = \frac{ka}{k}$, that is, $xy = a$; for, this strain leaves the ordinate y of each point unchanged, while it changes the abscissa x to $\frac{x}{k}$. In this way we see that *two successive strains of the plane with respective axes the x-axis and the y-axis and with respective coefficients k and $\frac{1}{k}$ transform the hyperbola $xy = a$ into itself.* The successive ap-

plication of these two strains results in a transformation which is known as a *hyperbolic rotation*. The term "hyperbolic rotation" is related to the fact that under such a transformation all the points of the hyperbola "slide" along the curve; thus, in Fig. 16 the point M is first transformed into the point M_1, and then M_1 is transformed into M'; that is, the effect of the hyperbolic rotation is to transform the point M of the hyperbola into the point M' of the same hyperbola. Such a transformation is analogous to a rotation—we might say that the hyperbola "rotates."

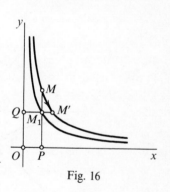

Fig. 16

Note the following properties of a hyperbolic rotation:

(a) *A hyperbolic rotation transforms a straight line into a straight line.* (This follows from property (a), section 2.)

(b) *A hyperbolic rotation transforms the coordinate axes* (*the asymptotes of the hyperbola*) *into themselves* (since each of the two strains which constitute the hyperbolic rotation transforms each coordinate axis into itself).

(c) *A hyperbolic rotation transforms parallel lines into parallel lines.* (This follows from property (b), section 2.)

(d) *A hyperbolic rotation does not change the ratio of the lengths of line segments lying on the same straight line.* (This follows from property (c), section 2.)

(e) *A hyperbolic rotation does not change the areas of figures in the plane.* (For, as a result of the first strain, all figures have their areas multiplied by k, and as a result of the second they are divided by k. This follows from property (d), section 2.)

It is very important to note that *by means of a suitable hyperbolic rotation it is possible to transform any point of the hyperbola into any other point on the same branch of the hyperbola.* In fact, the first strain transforms the point (x, y) of the hyperbola $xy = a$ into the point (x, ky) of the hyperbola $xy = ka$; then the second strain transforms the point (x, ky) of the hyperbola $xy = ka$ into the point $\left(\dfrac{x}{k}, ky\right)$ of the original hyperbola (see Fig. 16). Thus, the net effect of the hyperbolic rotation is to transform the point (x, y) of the hyperbola $xy = a$ into the point $\left(\dfrac{x}{k}, ky\right)$. From this it follows that by means of a suitable hyperbolic rotation it is possible to transform the point (x, y) of the hyperbola $xy = a$ into any other point (x_1, y_1) of the same branch of the hyperbola, for we need only choose k so as to have

$$x_1 = \frac{x}{k} \quad \text{or} \quad k = \frac{x}{x_1}.$$

Then

$$y_1 = \frac{a}{x_1}.$$

5. PROPERTIES OF THE HYPERBOLA

By using hyperbolic rotations it is possible to establish a number of interesting geometric properties of the hyperbola. To begin with we shall discuss chords and tangents of the hyperbola.

A straight line which intersects a hyperbola at two points is called a *secant* of that hyperbola. That segment of a secant whose end points lie on the hyperbola is called a *chord* of the hyperbola. The secants of a hyperbola are of two types: those that intersect only one branch of the hyperbola and those that intersect both

11

branches (see UV and U_1V_1 in Fig. 17); a similar remark holds for chords. Now let us consider a secant of the first type and the

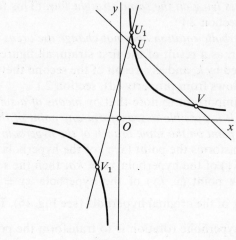

Fig. 17

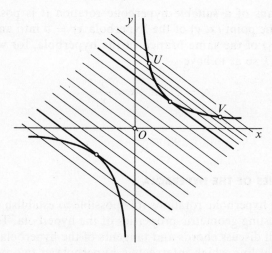

Fig. 18

straight lines parallel to it (Fig. 18). Among these will be some which intersect the hyperbola at two points, some which do not intersect the hyperbola at all, and finally, some which intersect the hyperbola in exactly one point; a line of the latter type is called a *tangent* of the hyperbola.[1]

A hyperbolic rotation will transform a chord UV of the hyperbola into a new chord $U'V'$, and if U and V are points on the same branch (or on different branches) of the hyperbola, then U' and V' will also lie on the same branch (or on different branches). The former case is shown in Fig. 19.

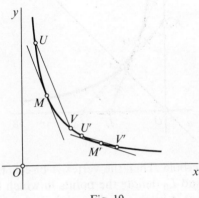

Fig. 19

Under the hyperbolic rotation which transforms a point M of the hyperbola into a point M' of the hyperbola, the tangent to the hyperbola at the point M is transformed into the tangent at the point M'. To prove this, consider a chord UV which is parallel to the tangent at the point M (Fig. 19). Chord UV is transformed into a chord $U'V'$, while a straight line parallel to UV and having only the one point, M, in common with the hyperbola is transformed into a straight line parallel to $U'V'$ having only one point, M', in common with the hyperbola, that is, the tangent at the point M' (from property (*c*) of section 4).

---

[1] We could also define a tangent to a hyperbola as a straight line which has precisely one point in common with the hyperbola and is parallel to neither asymptote. (A straight line parallel to an asymptote does intersect the hyperbola in only one point but is not a tangent.)

We now proceed to consider some properties of the hyperbola.

(1) *If a line is tangent to a hyperbola, then the point of tangency bisects that segment of the tangent line having its end points on the asymptotes of the hyperbola.*

The line *aa* which bisects the angle formed by the coordinate axes is an axis of symmetry of the hyperbola (Fig. 20). Let A be a

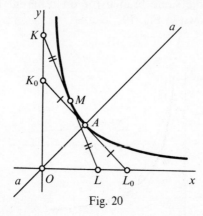

Fig. 20

vertex of the hyperbola. Then the vertex A bisects the line segment K_0L_0, where K_0 and L_0 denote the points in which the line tangent to the hyperbola at A intersects the x-axis and y-axis, respectively (because of the symmetry with respect to the axis *aa*). Now let M be a point of the hyperbola distinct from A; denote by L and K, respectively, the points of intersection of the tangent through M with the x-axis and y-axis. Let us apply the hyperbolic rotation which transforms the point A into the point M. This rotation transforms the segment K_0L_0 into the segment KL (as a result of properties (a) and (b), section 4). But under a hyperbolic rotation the mid-point of a segment is transformed into the mid-point of the transformed segment (property (d), section 4); hence, M is the mid-point of the segment KL.

(2) *The area of the triangle formed by a tangent to the hyperbola $xy = a$ and the coordinate axes is the same for all tangents.*

In order to prove this, consider a triangle KOL formed by the tangent at a point M of the hyperbola and the coordinate axes (Fig. 20). The hyperbolic rotation which transforms the point M into the point A transforms the triangle KOL into the triangle K_0OL_0 (the points A, K_0, and L_0 as in property (1) above). Using property (e), section 4, we have $S_{\triangle KOL} = S_{\triangle K_0OL_0}$; that is, the area of the triangle KOL is independent of our choice of the point M.

From properties (1) and (2) it follows that a hyperbola can be defined as *the locus of the mid-points of those line segments which, together with the coordinate axes, form right triangles of given area* (Fig. 21).

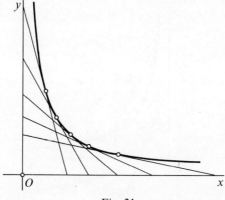

Fig. 21

(3) *The mid-points of a series of parallel chords of a hyperbola lie on a single straight line which passes through the center of the hyperbola.*

Let UV be any chord of the hyperbola (Fig. 22a), S its mid-point, and T be the point in which the straight line OS inter-

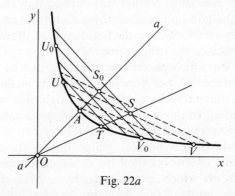

Fig. 22a

sects the hyperbola.[1] Apply the hyperbolic rotation which transforms the point T into the vertex A of the hyperbola. This transformation transforms the line OT into the axis aa of the hyperbola,

---

[1] We shall restrict ourselves here to the case in which U and V lie on the same branch of the hyperbola, for this is the only case of the result that we require for the following developments. We leave to the reader the investigation of the case in which U and V lie on different branches of the hyperbola.

and the chord UV into the chord U_0V_0 which is bisected by the axis of symmetry aa. But this is possible only if U_0V_0 is perpendicular to aa. Indeed, suppose U_0V_0 is not perpendicular to aa (Fig.

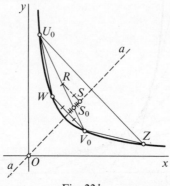

Fig. 22*b*

22*b*). Let us draw chords U_0Z and V_0W perpendicular to aa. Since the line aa is an axis of symmetry of the hyperbola, U_0ZV_0W is an isosceles trapezoid having aa as an axis of symmetry ($U_0W = V_0Z$). But the axis of symmetry of such a trapezoid cannot bisect its diagonal U_0V_0 (thus, $V_0S_0 = S_0R < S_0U_0$), which is a contradiction. Now all chords parallel to UV are transformed into chords parallel to U_0V_0, and the mid-points of all these chords lie on the straight line aa. From this it follows that the mid-points of all chords parallel to the chord UV lie on the straight line OT.

A straight line which passes through the center of a hyperbola is called a *diameter* of that hyperbola. (This is analogous to the definition of a diameter of a circle as a straight line which passes through its center.) In this booklet, the diameter is taken to be the entire straight line and not merely a segment of it.

The diameter of a hyperbola which bisects the chords in a family of parallel chords is called the *conjugate* diameter of those chords; the chords which are bisected by a given diameter are called *conjugate* chords of that diameter. In what follows we shall have occasion to speak of the *radii* of a given hyperbola, by which we mean either of the two segments of a diameter determined by the center of the hyperbola and the points of intersection of the diameter with the hyperbola. (The radii of a hyperbola are defined analogously to radii of circles.)

16

Note that circles possess a property analogous to property (3) of hyperbolas: *The mid-points of a family of parallel chords of a given circle lie on a single straight line which passes through the center of the circle*; in fact, they lie on the diameter of the circle which is perpendicular to those chords (Fig. 23).

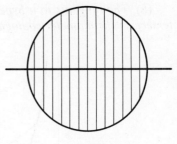

Fig. 23

(4) *The straight lines passing through the end points of a given chord of the hyperbola and parallel to the asymptotes intersect on the diameter conjugate to that chord.*

Let UV be a chord of the hyperbola, S its mid-point, and T the point of intersection of the straight line OS with the hyperbola (Fig. 24). Let us apply the hyperbolic rotation transforming the

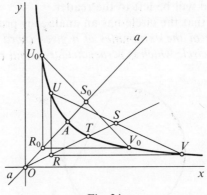

Fig. 24

point T into the vertex A of the hyperbola. Under this rotation the chord UV will be transformed into the chord $U_0 V_0$ perpendicular to the axis aa (see the proof of property (3)). The straight lines UR and VR are parallel to the asymptotes and will be transformed into straight lines $U_0 R_0$ and $V_0 R_0$, also parallel to the asymptotes (see properties (b) and (c), section 4). Since aa is an axis of symmetry of the hyperbola and bisects the angle formed by the asymptotes, the point of intersection R_0 of the straight lines $U_0 R_0$ and $V_0 R_0$ lies on aa. From this it follows that the point of intersection R of the straight lines UR and VR lies on the diameter OT.

17

(5) *The tangents to a hyperbola at the ends of a given chord intersect on the diameter conjugate to that chord* (Fig. 25a).

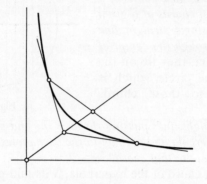

Fig. 25a

The proof of property (5) is entirely analogous to the proof of property (4) and will be left to the reader.

Let us note that the circle has an analogous property: *The tangents to a circle at the extremities of a given chord intersect on the diameter of the circle which is perpendicular to that chord* (Fig. 25b).

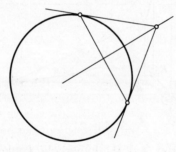

Fig. 25b

2. Hyperbolic Functions

6. THE UNIT HYPERBOLA AND ITS EQUATION

In section 3 we defined a hyperbola to be the graph of the equation $xy = a$. Then the coordinate axes were asymptotes of the hyperbola. We shall now find out what the equation of this hyperbola is in a new coordinate system in which the axes of the hyperbola are taken to be the coordinate axes.

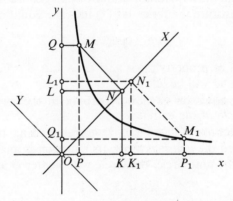

Fig. 26

Let M be a point on the hyperbola (Fig. 26), and suppose that its coordinates are x and y in our original coordinate system and X and Y in the new one. We shall now derive formulas relating x, y and X, Y. Let N be the projection of the point M on the axis OX, and let P, Q and K, L be the projections of M and N on the original x-axis and y-axis, respectively. Then

$$OP = OK - PK = ON \cos 45° - NM \cos 45°,$$
$$OQ = OL + LQ = ON \cos 45° + NM \cos 45°,$$

since the axes of a hyperbola $xy = a$ form angles of $45°$ with the asymptotes of the hyperbola. But $OP = x$, $OQ = y$, $ON = X$, and $NM = Y$; hence we obtain

$$x = (X - Y)\frac{\sqrt{2}}{2}, \qquad y = (X + Y)\frac{\sqrt{2}}{2}. \qquad (*)$$

If the point M lies below the axis aa, say at the position M_1 (Fig. 26), then we have

$$x_1 = OP_1 = OK_1 + K_1P_1 = ON_1 \cos 45° + N_1M_1 \cos 45°$$
$$= X_1 \frac{\sqrt{2}}{2} + (-Y_1) \frac{\sqrt{2}}{2},$$
$$y_1 = OQ_1 = OL_1 - Q_1L_1 = ON_1 \cos 45° - N_1M_1 \cos 45°$$
$$= X_1 \frac{\sqrt{2}}{2} - (-Y_1) \frac{\sqrt{2}}{2}.$$

These are exactly the same as formulas (*). The reader should also verify that formulas (*) hold for the other branch of the hyperbola, which is in the third quadrant of our original coordinate system.

If we substitute the formulas (*) into the equation $xy = a$, we obtain

$$(X^2 - Y^2) \cdot \frac{1}{2} = a,$$

that is,

$$X^2 - Y^2 = 2a,$$

which is the equation of our hyperbola in the new coordinate system.

The hyperbola $X^2 - Y^2 = 1$, corresponding to the choice $a = \frac{1}{2}$, is called the *unit hyperbola*. Its equation is analogous to the equation of the unit circle, the circle with center O and radius 1:[1]

$$X^2 + Y^2 = 1.$$

In the original coordinate system, the equation of the unit hyperbola is, of course, $xy = \frac{1}{2}$, since $a = \frac{1}{2}$.

7. THE HYPERBOLIC FUNCTIONS

Let us now proceed to develop the theory of hyperbolic functions—a theory which in many respects is analogous to the theory of the trigonometric (circular) functions. In order to emphasize the analogy between trigonometric and hyperbolic functions, we shall conduct almost the entire exposition in two parallel columns: On the left we shall list well-known results from the theory of trigonometric functions, while on the right we shall give the analogous results from the theory of hyperbolic functions.

[1] Let M be an arbitrary point of the unit circle (Fig. 27a), and let X and Y be its co-ordinates. By the Pythagorean theorem we have $OP^2 + PM^2 = OM^2$, that is, $X^2 + Y^2 = 1$.

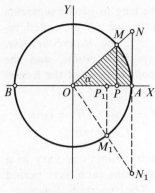

Fig. 27a

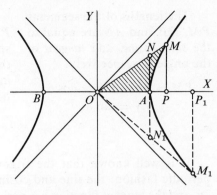

Fig. 27b

Consider the unit circle (Fig. 27a)

$$X^2 + Y^2 = 1.$$

If M is a point of the unit circle, then the measure of *angle α* (in radians) between the radii OA and OM is defined to be the length of the arc AM or, alternatively, twice the area of the sector AOM determined by the arc AM and the radii OA and OM.

From the point M on the unit circle drop the perpendicular MP to the diameter OA. At the point A draw a line tangent to the unit circle; let N be the point of intersection of this tangent with the diameter OM.

Consider the unit hyperbola (Fig. 27b)

$$X^2 - Y^2 = 1.$$

If M is a point of the unit hyperbola, then the measure of *hyperbolic angle t* between the radii OA and OM is defined to be twice the area of the sector AOM determined by the arc AM of the hyperbola and the radii OA and OM.[1]

From the point M on the unit hyperbola drop the perpendicular MP to the diameter OA. The diameter OA is an axis of symmetry of the hyperbola, and the point A is a vertex of the hyperbola. At the point A draw a line tangent to the hyperbola; let N be the point of intersection of this tangent with the diameter OM.

---

[1] A fundamental property of the angle α of the circle is that α is not changed by a rigid rotation of the sector AOM about the origin O. The analogous property of the hyperbolic angle t is also true; that is, t is not changed by a hyperbolic rotation of the sector AOM (see property (e), section 4).

The lengths of the segments PM, OP, and AN are equal to the *sine, cosine,* and *tangent* of the angle α, respectively:

$$PM = \sin \alpha,\; OP = \cos \alpha,$$
$$AN = \tan \alpha.$$

The lengths of the segments PM, OP, and AN are called, respectively, the *hyperbolic sine,* the *hyperbolic cosine,* and the *hyperbolic tangent* of the hyperbolic angle t; we write[1]

$$PM = \sinh t,\; OP = \cosh t,$$
$$AN = \tanh t.$$

It is well known that the trigonometric functions vary in a periodic fashion: the sine and cosine functions each have period 2π, and the tangent function has period π. The hyperbolic functions, however, are not periodic.

The "hyperbolic angle" t may assume any value from 0 to ∞. In view of the definition of hyperbolic angles, this amounts to saying that for each positive number there is some hyperbolic sector AOM whose area is equal to that number. In order to prove this, let us consider an arbitrary hyperbolic angle AOM_1 of magnitude t_1, say. Let us apply the hyperbolic rotation that transforms the point A into the point M_1. Under this transformation the point M_1 is itself transformed into some point M_2; M_2 is transformed into some point M_3; M_3 into some point M_4; and so on (Fig. 28). It follows

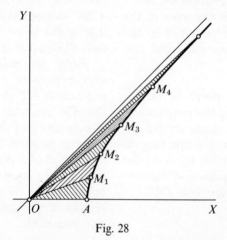

Fig. 28

[1] The ratios $\dfrac{1}{PM}$, $\dfrac{1}{OP}$, and $\dfrac{1}{AN}$ are sometimes called the *hyperbolic cosecant,* the *hyperbolic secant,* and the *hyperbolic cotangent* of the hyperbolic angle t. They are abbreviated csch t, sech t, and coth t.

from property (e), section 4, that the areas of the hyperbolic sectors AOM_1, M_1OM_2, M_2OM_3, M_3OM_4, . . . are equal; consequently, the hyperbolic angles AOM_1, AOM_2, AOM_3, AOM_4, . . . are equal to t_1, $2t_1$, $3t_1$, $4t_1$, . . . respectively. Hence, there exist arbitrarily large hyperbolic angles. As the point M on the hyperbola varies from A to M_1, M_1 to M_2, and so on, the hyperbolic angle t varies from 0 to t_1, t_1 to $2t_1$, and so on; hence, there are hyperbolic angles of any positive magnitude. (Remember that a "hyperbolic angle" is not an ordinary angle.)

From the definition of hyperbolic functions (Fig. 27b), it is easy to see that as the hyperbolic angle t varies from 0 to ∞, sinh t varies from 0 to ∞, cosh t varies from 1 to ∞, and tanh t varies from 0 to 1. Analogously to the trigonometric functions, we consider hyperbolic functions of negative hyperbolic angles (AOM_1, Fig. 27b); the angle AOM_1 is defined to be equal to $-t_1$, where t_1 is twice the area of the sector AOM_1. Then we have

$$\sinh(-t_1) = -M_1P_1 = -\sinh t_1,$$
$$\cosh(-t_1) = OP_1 = \cosh t_1,$$
$$\tanh(-t_1) = -N_1A = -\tanh t_1.$$

The graphs of the hyperbolic functions are shown in Fig. 29. Let

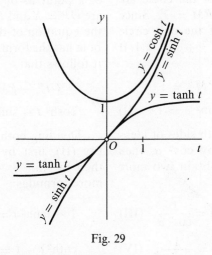

Fig. 29

us also note that sinh $0 = $ tanh $0 = 0$ and cosh $0 = 1$; these are analogous to sin $0 = $ tan $0 = 0$ and cos $0 = 1$.

8. IDENTITIES BETWEEN HYPERBOLIC FUNCTIONS

Let us now derive some fundamental trigonometric identities, together with the corresponding identities between hyperbolic functions.

From the similarity of the triangles OPM and OAN (Fig. 27a) it follows that

$$\frac{AN}{OA} = \frac{PM}{OP}.$$

But $\dfrac{AN}{OA} = \tan \alpha$ (since $OA = 1$), while

$$\frac{PM}{OP} = \frac{\sin \alpha}{\cos \alpha}.$$

In this way we obtain

$$\tan \alpha = \frac{\sin \alpha}{\cos \alpha}. \qquad \text{(I)}$$

Furthermore, the coordinates of a point M of the circle are $OP = X$ and $PM = Y$. Since the equation of the unit circle has the form $X^2 + Y^2 = 1$, it follows that

$$OP^2 + PM^2 = 1,$$
or
$$\cos^2 \alpha + \sin^2 \alpha = 1. \qquad \text{(II)}$$

Dividing both sides of identity (II), first by $\cos^2 \alpha$, then by $\sin^2 \alpha$, we obtain two more formulas:

$$1 + \tan^2 \alpha = \frac{1}{\cos^2 \alpha}, \qquad \text{(III)}$$

$$\cot^2 \alpha + 1 = \frac{1}{\sin^2 \alpha}. \qquad \text{(IV)}$$

From the similarity of the triangles OPM and OAN (Fig. 27b) it follows that

$$\frac{AN}{OA} = \frac{PM}{OP}.$$

But $\dfrac{AN}{OA} = \tanh t$ (since $OA = 1$), while

$$\frac{PM}{OP} = \frac{\sinh t}{\cosh t}.$$

In this way we obtain

$$\tanh t = \frac{\sinh t}{\cosh t}. \qquad \text{(I)}$$

Furthermore, the coordinates of a point M of the hyperbola are $OP = X$ and $PM = Y$. Since the equation of the unit hyperbola has the form $X^2 - Y^2 = 1$, it follows that

$$OP^2 - PM^2 = 1,$$
or
$$\cosh^2 t - \sinh^2 t = 1. \qquad \text{(II)}$$

Dividing both sides of identity (II), first by $\cosh^2 t$, and then by $\sinh^2 t$, we obtain two more formulas:

$$1 - \tanh^2 t = \frac{1}{\cosh^2 t}, \qquad \text{(III)}$$

$$\coth^2 t - 1 = \frac{1}{\sinh^2 t}. \qquad \text{(IV)}$$

Let us now derive the formulas for trigonometric and hyperbolic functions of the sum of two angles.

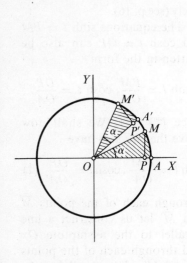

Fig. 30*a*

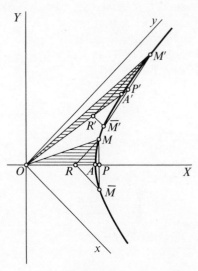

Fig. 30*b*

By a rigid rotation about the point O, let us transform the radii OA and OM of the circle into the radii OA' and OM' (Fig. 30*a*). Moreover, let segments PM and OP be transformed by this rotation into segments $P'M'$ and OP', respectively; $M'P'$ is clearly perpendicular to the radius OA'. Let $\alpha =$ angle AOM; then, since $P'M' = PM$ and $OP' = OP$ (rotation about O does not change the lengths of segments), we can use the equalities $\sin\alpha = PM$ and $\cos\alpha = OP$ to obtain

$$\sin\alpha = P'M',$$
$$\cos\alpha = OP'.$$

By applying a hyperbolic rotation, let us transform the radii OA and OM of the hyperbola into the radii OA' and OM' (Fig. 30*b*). The hyperbolic angles AOM and $A'OM'$ are then equal (property (e), section 4). Let these hyperbolic angles be equal to t. Moreover, let segments PM and OP be transformed by this rotation into segments $P'M'$ and OP', respectively. Let $\overline{M}$ and $\overline{M}'$ be the points at which MP and $M'P'$ intersect the hyperbola. Then $MP = P\overline{M}$, since OA is an axis of symmetry of the hyperbola, and $M'P' = P'\overline{M}'$ (using the equality $MP = P\overline{M}$ and property (d), section 4). In other

25

words, the chords $M\overline{M}$ and $M'\overline{M}'$ are conjugates of the diameters OP and OP', respectively (see p. 16).

The equations $\sinh t = PM$ and $\cosh t = OP$ can also be written in the form

$$\sinh t = \frac{PM}{OA}, \cosh t = \frac{OP}{OA},$$

since $OA = 1$. We shall now prove that we also have

$$\sinh t = \frac{P'M'}{OA'}, \cosh t = \frac{OP'}{OA'}. \quad (1)$$

Through each of the points $\overline{M}$ and $\overline{M}'$ let us construct a line parallel to the asymptote Ox and through each of the points M and M' a line parallel to the asymptote Oy (Fig. 30b). It follows from property (4), section 5, that the points of intersection, R and R', lie on the diameters OA and OA', respectively.

The triangles $MR\overline{M}$ and $M'R'\overline{M}'$ are right triangles, since the asymptotes Ox and Oy are perpendicular. Also, the points P and P' are the mid-points of the hypotenuses of these triangles. Using the theorem from plane geometry which states that the mid-point of the hypotenuse of a right triangle is equidistant from the vertices of the triangle, we have

$$PM = \overline{M}P = RP,$$
$$P'M' = \overline{M}'P' = R'P'.$$

Thus, we have

$$\sinh t = \frac{RP}{OA}, \cosh t = \frac{OP}{OA}.$$

But by the result stated in property (d), section 4,

$$\frac{RP}{OA} = \frac{R'P'}{OA'} = \frac{P'M'}{OA'}; \frac{OP}{OA} = \frac{OP'}{OA'},$$

from which (1) follows.

We now let $\angle AOM = \alpha$, and $\angle MOM' = \beta$ (Fig. 31a).

We now take two "hyperbolic angles," AOM equal to t, and MOM' equal to u (Fig. 31b).

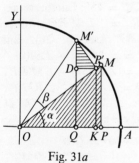

Fig. 31a

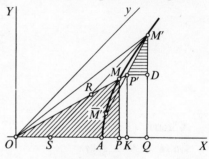

Fig. 31b

From the points M and M' drop the perpendiculars MP and $M'Q$ to OA. Also, from the point M' drop the perpendicular $M'P'$ to OM, and from the point P' drop the perpendiculars $P'D$ to $M'Q$ and $P'K$ to OA. In this way we obtain

$$\sin \alpha = PM, \quad \cos \alpha = OP;$$
$$\sin \beta = P'M', \cos \beta = OP';$$
$$\sin (\alpha + \beta) = QM',$$
$$\cos (\alpha + \beta) = OQ.$$

From the points M and M' drop the perpendiculars MP and $M'Q$ to OA; also, through the point M' draw the chord $M'\overline{M}'$ conjugate to OM (see p. 16). Let P' be the point of intersection of $M'\overline{M}'$ and OM; from the point P' drop the perpendiculars $P'D$ to $M'Q$ and $P'K$ to OA. In this way we obtain

$$\sinh t = PM, \cosh t = OP;$$
$$\sinh u = \frac{P'M'}{OM}, \cosh u = \frac{OP'}{OM};$$
$$\sinh (t + u) = QM',$$
$$\cosh (t + u) = OQ.$$

The right triangles OPM and $M'DP'$ are similar, because $\angle MOP = \angle P'M'D$ (the sides of these angles are mutually perpendicular).

The triangles OPM and OKP' are similar, since they are both right triangles and have a common angle.

The triangles OPM and $M'DP'$ are also similar: they are both right triangles, and we can show that $\angle MOP = \angle P'M'D$. For, the straight line $M'R$ parallel to the asymptote Oy of the hyperbola intersects the diameter OM in the point R and the axis OA in the point S; therefore, $\angle QM'S = \angle QSM' = 45°$. Furthermore, $\angle P'M'R = \angle M'RP'$, since $P'M' = RP'$ (see p. 26). But
$$\angle MOP = \angle M'SQ - \angle SRO$$
$$= \angle M'SQ - \angle M'RP',$$
$$\angle P'M'D = \angle SM'Q - \angle RM'P';$$
therefore, $\angle MOP = \angle P'M'D$.

Clearly (Fig. 31*a*),
$$\sin(\alpha + \beta) = QM'$$
$$= KP' + DM',$$
$$\cos(\alpha + \beta) = OQ$$
$$= OK - DP'.$$

Clearly (Fig. 31*b*),
$$\sinh(t + u) = QM'$$
$$= KP' + DM',$$
$$\cosh(t + u) = OQ$$
$$= OK + P'D.$$

From the similarity of the triangles OPM and OKP':

$$\frac{KP'}{OP'} = \frac{PM}{OM}, \; KP' = \frac{OP'}{OM} \cdot PM;$$

$$\frac{OK}{OP'} = \frac{OP}{OM}, \; OK = \frac{OP'}{OM} \cdot OP.$$

From the similarity of the triangles OPM and OKP':

$$\frac{KP'}{OP'} = \frac{PM}{OM}, \; KP' = \frac{OP'}{OM} \cdot PM;$$

$$\frac{OK}{OP'} = \frac{OP}{OM}, \; OK = \frac{OP'}{OM} \cdot OP.$$

From the similarity of the triangles OPM and $M'DP'$:

$$\frac{DM'}{P'M'} = \frac{OP}{OM}, \; DM' = \frac{P'M'}{OM} \cdot OP;$$

$$\frac{DP'}{P'M'} = \frac{PM}{OM}, \; DP' = \frac{P'M'}{OM} \cdot PM.$$

From the similarity of the triangles OPM and $M'DP'$:

$$\frac{DM'}{P'M'} = \frac{OP}{OM}, \; DM' = \frac{P'M'}{OM} \cdot OP;$$

$$\frac{P'D}{P'M'} = \frac{PM}{OM}, \; P'D = \frac{P'M'}{OM} \cdot PM.$$

Finally, if we take into account that

$$PM = \sin \alpha, \quad OP = \cos \alpha,$$

$$\frac{P'M'}{OM} = \sin \beta, \quad \frac{OP'}{OM} = \cos \beta,$$

we obtain

$$\sin (\alpha + \beta) = \sin \alpha \cos \beta$$
$$+ \cos \alpha \sin \beta, \text{ (V)}$$
$$\cos (\alpha + \beta) = \cos \alpha \cos \beta$$
$$- \sin \alpha \sin \beta. \text{ (VI)}$$

All of the other formulas of the theory of trigonometric functions follow from formulas (V), (VI), and formulas (I), (II) of section 8.

For instance, we have

$$\tan (\alpha + \beta) = \frac{\sin (\alpha + \beta)}{\cos (\alpha + \beta)}$$
$$= \frac{\sin \alpha \cos \beta + \cos \alpha \sin \beta}{\cos \alpha \cos \beta - \sin \alpha \sin \beta}.$$

Dividing the numerator and the denominator of the right-hand side of the preceding equality by $\cos \alpha \cos \beta$, we obtain

$$\tan (\alpha + \beta)$$
$$= \frac{\tan \alpha + \tan \beta}{1 - \tan \alpha \tan \beta}. \quad \text{(VII)}$$

If $\beta = \alpha$, then formulas (V), (VI), and (VII) will take the form

$$\sin 2\alpha = 2 \sin \alpha \cos \alpha, \quad \text{(VIII)}$$
$$\cos 2\alpha = \cos^2 \alpha - \sin^2 \alpha, \quad \text{(IX)}$$
$$\tan 2\alpha = \frac{2 \tan \alpha}{1 - \tan^2 \alpha}. \quad \text{(X)}$$

Finally, if we take into account that

$$PM = \sinh t, \quad OP = \cosh t,$$

$$\frac{P'M'}{OM} = \sinh u, \quad \frac{OP'}{OM} = \cosh u,$$

we obtain

$$\sinh (t + u) = \sinh t \cosh u$$
$$+ \cosh t \sinh u, \text{ (V)}$$
$$\cosh (t + u) = \cosh t \cosh u$$
$$+ \sinh t \sinh u. \text{ (VI)}$$

All of the other formulas of the theory of hyperbolic functions follow from formulas (V), (VI), and formulas (I), (II) of section 8.

For instance, we have

$$\tanh (t + u) = \frac{\sinh (t + u)}{\cosh (t + u)}$$
$$= \frac{\sinh t \cosh u + \cosh t \sinh u}{\cosh t \cosh u + \sinh t \sinh u}.$$

Dividing the numerator and the denominator of the right-hand side of the preceding equality by $\cosh t \cosh u$, we obtain

$$\tanh (t + u)$$
$$= \frac{\tanh t + \tanh u}{1 + \tanh t \tanh u}. \quad \text{(VII)}$$

If $u = t$, then formulas (V), (VI), and (VII) will take the form

$$\sinh 2t = 2 \sinh t \cosh t. \quad \text{(VIII)}$$
$$\cosh 2t = \cosh^2 t + \sinh^2 t, \text{(IX)}$$
$$\tanh 2t = \frac{2 \tanh t}{1 + \tanh^2 t}. \quad \text{(X)}$$

From formulas (V) and (VI) we obtain

$$\sin \alpha = \sin (\alpha + \beta) \cos \beta$$
$$- \cos (\alpha + \beta) \sin \beta,$$
$$\cos \alpha = \cos (\alpha + \beta) \cos \beta$$
$$+ \sin (\alpha + \beta) \sin \beta.$$

If in the last two formulas we replace $\alpha + \beta$ by α and α by $\alpha - \beta$, the formulas take the form

$$\sin (\alpha - \beta) = \sin \alpha \cos \beta$$
$$- \cos \alpha \sin \beta, \quad \text{(XI)}$$
$$\cos (\alpha - \beta) = \cos \alpha \cos \beta$$
$$+ \sin \alpha \sin \beta. \quad \text{(XII)}$$

Dividing formula (XI) by formula (XII), we obtain

$$\tan (\alpha - \beta)$$
$$= \frac{\tan \alpha - \tan \beta}{1 + \tan \alpha \tan \beta}. \quad \text{(XIII)}$$

Let us also express $\sin \alpha$, $\cos \alpha$, and $\tan \alpha$ in terms of $\tan \frac{\alpha}{2}$. From formulas (VIII)–(X) and (III) it follows that

$$\sin \alpha = 2 \sin \frac{\alpha}{2} \cdot \cos \frac{\alpha}{2}$$

$$= 2 \frac{\sin \frac{\alpha}{2}}{\cos \frac{\alpha}{2}} \cdot \cos^2 \frac{\alpha}{2}$$

$$= 2 \tan \frac{\alpha}{2} \cdot \frac{1}{\dfrac{1}{\cos^2 \frac{\alpha}{2}}}$$

$$= \frac{2 \tan \frac{\alpha}{2}}{1 + \tan^2 \frac{\alpha}{2}}; \quad \text{(XIV)}$$

From formulas (V) and (VI) we obtain

$$\sinh t = \sinh (t + u) \cosh u$$
$$- \cosh (t + u) \sinh u,$$
$$\cosh t = \cosh (t + u) \cosh u$$
$$- \sinh (t + u) \sinh u.$$

If in the last two formulas we replace $t + u$ by t and t by $t - u$, the formulas take the form

$$\sinh (t - u) = \sinh t \cosh u$$
$$- \cosh t \sinh u, \quad \text{(XI)}$$
$$\cosh (t - u) = \cosh t \cosh u$$
$$- \sinh t \sinh u. \quad \text{(XII)}$$

Dividing formula (XI) by formula (XII), we obtain

$$\tanh (t - u)$$
$$= \frac{\tanh t - \tanh u}{1 - \tanh t \tanh u}. \quad \text{(XIII)}$$

Let us also express $\sinh t$, $\cosh t$, and $\tanh t$ in terms of $\tanh \frac{t}{2}$. From formulas (VIII)–(X) and (III) it follows that

$$\sinh t = 2 \sinh \frac{t}{2} \cosh \frac{t}{2}$$

$$= 2 \frac{\sinh \frac{t}{2}}{\cosh \frac{t}{2}} \cdot \cosh^2 \frac{t}{2}$$

$$= 2 \tanh \frac{t}{2} \cdot \frac{1}{\dfrac{1}{\cosh^2 \frac{t}{2}}}$$

$$= \frac{2 \tanh \frac{t}{2}}{1 - \tanh^2 \frac{t}{2}}; \quad \text{(XIV)}$$

$$\cos\alpha = \cos^2\frac{\alpha}{2} - \sin^2\frac{\alpha}{2} \qquad\qquad \cosh t = \cosh^2\frac{t}{2} + \sinh^2\frac{t}{2}$$

$$= \cos^2\frac{\alpha}{2}\left(1 - \frac{\sin^2\frac{\alpha}{2}}{\cos^2\frac{\alpha}{2}}\right) \qquad = \cosh^2\frac{t}{2}\left(1 + \frac{\sinh^2\frac{t}{2}}{\cosh^2\frac{t}{2}}\right)$$

$$= \frac{1}{\dfrac{1}{\cos^2\frac{\alpha}{2}}}\left(1 - \tan^2\frac{\alpha}{2}\right) \qquad = \frac{1}{\dfrac{1}{\cosh^2\frac{t}{2}}}\left(1 + \tanh^2\frac{t}{2}\right)$$

$$= \frac{1 - \tan^2\frac{\alpha}{2}}{1 + \tan^2\frac{\alpha}{2}}; \qquad \text{(XV)} \qquad = \frac{1 + \tanh^2\frac{t}{2}}{1 - \tanh^2\frac{t}{2}}; \qquad \text{(XV)}$$

and   and

$$\tan\alpha = \frac{2\tan\frac{\alpha}{2}}{1 - \tan^2\frac{\alpha}{2}}. \quad \text{(XVI)} \qquad \tanh t = \frac{2\tanh\frac{t}{2}}{1 + \tanh^2\frac{t}{2}}. \quad \text{(XVI)}$$

Let us note that in the derivation of the addition formulas for the hyperbolic functions it was not essential to measure the first angle t from the axis of symmetry OA of the hyperbola; almost exactly as above it is possible to derive formulas (V) and (VI) for an arbitrary position of the diameter OA. Indeed, if in Fig. 32 we take the angles AOM and MOM' to be the angles t and u, respectively, then MP and $M'Q$ are conjugates of OA, and $M'P'$ is a conjugate of OM. Therefore,

$$\sinh t = \frac{PM}{OA}, \quad \cosh t = \frac{OP}{OA},$$

$$\sinh u = \frac{P'M'}{OM}, \quad \cosh u = \frac{OP'}{OM},$$

$$\sinh(t+u) = \frac{QM'}{OA},$$

$$\cosh(t+u) = \frac{OQ}{OA},$$

which imply formulas (V) and (VI), as above.

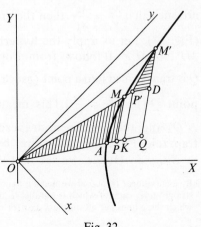

Fig. 32

3. Natural Logarithms

9. LOGARITHMS AND THE HYPERBOLA

Consider the hyperbola $xy = 1$ (Fig. 33). On this hyperbola take two arbitrary points M and N and from them drop perpen-

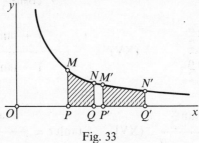

Fig. 33

diculars MP and NQ to the x-axis. Consider the curvilinear trapezoid $PQNM$.[1] The area S_{PQNM} of this trapezoid depends on the abscissas $OP = x_1$ and $OQ = x_2$ of the points M and N ($x_2 > x_1$). We shall now determine just how S_{PQNM} depends on x_1 and x_2, that is, how to calculate S_{PQNM}, given x_1 and x_2.

To begin with, we prove that *the area S_{PQNM} depends only on the ratio $\frac{x_2}{x_1}$*. In other words, we prove that if two curvilinear trapezoids $PQNM$ ($OP = x_1$, $OQ = x_2$) and $P'Q'N'M'$ ($OP' = x_1'$, $OQ' = x_2'$) are such that $\frac{x_2}{x_1} = \frac{x_2'}{x_1'}$, then the areas of these trapezoids are equal (Fig. 33). Let us apply the hyperbolic rotation which transforms MP into $M'P'$. It follows from property (d), section 4, that the point Q is transformed into a point $\overline{Q}$ such that $\frac{O\overline{Q}}{OP'} = \frac{OQ}{OP}$, that is, into the point $Q'\left(\text{for } \frac{x_2'}{x_1'} = \frac{x_2}{x_1}\right)$. This means that NQ is transformed into $N'Q'$ and the curvilinear trapezoid $PQNM$ into the curvilinear trapezoid $P'Q'N'M'$; therefore, by property (e), section 4, $S_{PQNM} = S_{P'Q'N'M'}$. Hence, we see that the area S_{PQNM} depends only on

---

[1] By a curvilinear trapezoid we mean a figure bounded by an arc of a curved line, two straight lines each of which is parallel to the y-axis (or the x-axis), and the segment which these lines cut off on the x-axis (or the y-axis).

the ratio $\dfrac{x_2}{x_1} = z$; that is, S_{PQNM} is a function of z, and we write

$$S_{PQNM} = S\left(\frac{x_2}{x_1}\right) = S(z).$$

Since $\dfrac{z}{1} = z$, $S(z)$ is the area of the curvilinear trapezoid bounded by the hyperbola, the x-axis, and the straight lines $x = 1$ and $x = z$.

The function $S(z)$ is defined for any value of z greater than 1. From our geometric interpretation it follows that $S(z)$ is an increasing function (that is, if $z_1 > z_2$, then $S(z_1) > S(z_2)$) and continuous (values of $S(z)$ near $S(z_0)$ correspond to values of z near z_0). It is natural to define $S(1)$ to be 0, for if $z = 1$, the trapezoid is simply a line segment. For sufficiently large values of z the values of the function $S(z)$ may be as large as we please. The proof of this fact is completely analogous to the proof of the fact that a hyperbolic angle exists which is as large as we please (pp. 22–23). Thus, there must exist a number $z > 1$ such that $S(z) = 1$. We shall call this number e:

$$S(e) = 1.$$

We shall compute the value of e later (see Fig. 35).

Let us now find a formula for the function $S(z)$. We shall prove first of all that for any two numbers z_1 and z_2 greater than 1,

$$S(z_1) + S(z_2) = S(z_1 z_2).$$

(If $z_1 = 1$, then the relation obviously holds, because $S(1) = 0$.) In general, $S(z_1)$ is the area of the curvilinear trapezoid KP_1M_1A, for which $OK = 1$, $OP_1 = z_1$ (Fig. 34); $S(z_2)$ is the area of the cur-

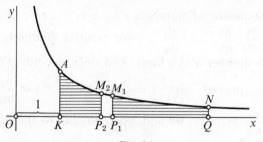

Fig. 34

vilinear trapezoid KP_2M_2A, for which $OP_2 = z_2$, or of the curvilinear trapezoid P_1QNM_1, for which $OP_1 = z_1$, $OQ = z_1 z_2$ (since $S(z_1 z_2/z_1) = S(z_2)$. From these remarks it follows that

$$S(z_1) + S(z_2) = S_{KP_1M_1A} + S_{P_1QNM_1} = S_{KQNA} = S(z_1 z_2).$$

We may use the relation just established to prove that for any positive number α,

$$S(z^\alpha) = \alpha S(z).$$

Let us consider separately a number of special cases.

If $\alpha = n$, where n is a positive integer, then we obtain successively

$$
\begin{aligned}
S(z^n) &= S(z \cdot z^{n-1}) = S(z) + S(z^{n-1}) \\
&= S(z) + S(z \cdot z^{n-2}) = 2S(z) + S(z^{n-2}) \\
&= 2S(z) + S(z \cdot z^{n-3}) = 3S(z) + S(z^{n-3}) \\
&= \ldots \\
&= (n-2)S(z) + S(z^2) \\
&= (n-2)S(z) + S(z \cdot z) = nS(z).
\end{aligned}
$$

If $\alpha = \dfrac{1}{m}$, where m is a positive integer, then, according to what has already been shown, we have

$$S(z) = S([z^{\frac{1}{m}}]^m) = mS(z^{\frac{1}{m}}), \text{ so that } S(z^{\frac{1}{m}}) = \frac{1}{m} S(z).$$

If $\alpha = \dfrac{n}{m}$, where m and n are positive integers, then, according to what has already been shown, we have

$$S(z^{\frac{n}{m}}) = S([z^{\frac{1}{m}}]^n) = n \cdot S(z^{\frac{1}{m}}) = n \cdot \frac{1}{m} S(z) = \frac{n}{m} S(z).$$

Finally, if α is a positive irrational number, then z^α is the limit of some sequence of numbers $z^{\frac{n_1}{m_1}}, z^{\frac{n_2}{m_2}}, \ldots, z^{\frac{n_k}{m_k}}, \ldots$, where the numbers $\dfrac{n_1}{m_1}, \dfrac{n_2}{m_2}, \ldots, \dfrac{n_k}{m_k}, \ldots$ are positive fractions which approach the number α as a limit. And since, according to what has just been proved, $S(z^{\frac{n_1}{m_1}}) = \dfrac{n_1}{m_1} S(z)$, $S(z^{\frac{n_2}{m_2}}) = \dfrac{n_2}{m_2} S(z), \ldots$, $S(z^{\frac{n_k}{m_k}}) = \dfrac{n_k}{m_k} S(z), \ldots$, we find, upon passing to the limit, that in this case also[1]

$$S(z^\alpha) = \alpha S(z).$$

---

[1] Here we make use of the continuity of the function $S(z)$. A rigorous argument would be somewhat more complex than the one we have given here.

Now, the properties

$$S(e) = 1,$$

$$S(z_1 z_2) = S(z_1) + S(z_2),$$

$$S(z^\alpha) = \alpha S(z),$$

are just the properties of logarithms to the base e.

For $z > 1$, we have

$$z = e^{\log_e z}.$$

Since $e > 1$ (see p. 33) and $\log_e z > 0$ (for $z > 1$), we have

$$S(z) = S(e^{\log_e z}) = \log_e z \cdot S(e) = \log_e z,$$

because $S(e) = 1$ by the definition of the number e. Thus, we finally obtain

$$S(z) = \log_e z.$$

This is the formula we wished to obtain.

From this formula follows the fact that the area of the curvilinear trapezoid $PQNM$ bounded by the hyperbola $xy = 1$, the x-axis, and the straight lines $x = x_1$ and $x = x_2$, where $x_2 > x_1$, is given by

$$\log_e \frac{x_2}{x_1}.$$

Thus, in connection with certain geometric considerations concerning areas, we have unexpectedly encountered logarithms. Here the system of logarithms is based on the number e, and not on an arbitrary number or on the number 10, as is the case with common logarithms. These remarks shed light on the fact that the two men who first dealt with the theory of logarithms, Napier and Bürgi, arrived independently at logarithms to the base e (and not logarithms to the base 10, which might appear to be the simplest). This same "geometric" definition of logarithms is related to the fact that logarithms to the base e often occur in problems of mathematics and physics which, at first glance, seem to have no relationship whatsoever to the logarithmic function.[1]

---

[1] For further information on the geometric definition of logarithms, see the booklet by A. I. Markushevich, *Areas and Logarithms*, in this series.

10. THE BASE e OF NATURAL LOGARITHMS

We shall now calculate the number e to a few decimal places.

In Fig. 35, $OK = 1$, $OP = 2$, and $OQ = 3$. The area, $S(2)$, of the curvilinear trapezoid $KPMA$ is less than the area of the

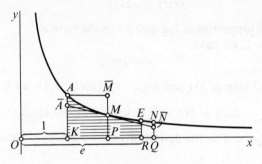

Fig. 35

rectangle $KP\overline{M}A$, which is $KA \cdot KP = 1 \cdot 1 = 1$. Thus,

$$S(2) < 1.$$

On the other hand, $S(3)$ is the area of the curvilinear trapezoid $KQNA$. This area is greater than the area of the trapezoid $KQ\overline{N}\overline{A}$ ($\overline{A}\overline{N}$ being the tangent to the hyperbola at the point M). Since $OP = 2$, $PM = \frac{1}{2}$, and the area of $KQ\overline{N}\overline{A} = PM \cdot KQ = 1$. Therefore, $S(3) > 1$. From the inequalities $S(2) < 1 < S(3)$ and since $S(z)$ is an increasing function, it follows that

$$2 < e < 3.$$

To calculate the value of e with greater precision, we consider the curvilinear trapezoid $KPMA$ (Fig. 36), where

$$OK = 1, \quad OP = 1 + \frac{1}{n}.$$

By what has been demonstrated above, the area of this trapezoid is

$$\log_e \left(1 + \frac{1}{n}\right).$$

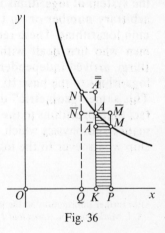

Fig. 36

The area of trapezoid $KPMA$ lies between the areas of the rectangles $KP\overline{M}A$ and $KPM\overline{A}$ shown in Fig. 36, that is, between

$$KA \cdot KP = 1 \cdot \frac{1}{n} = \frac{1}{n}$$

and

$$KP \cdot PM = \frac{1}{n} \cdot \frac{1}{1 + \frac{1}{n}}$$

$$= \frac{\frac{1}{n}}{\frac{n+1}{n}} = \frac{1}{n+1}.$$

Therefore,

$$\frac{1}{n} > \log_e\left(1 + \frac{1}{n}\right) > \frac{1}{n+1}.$$

From the latter inequalities we obtain

$$1 > n \log_e\left(1 + \frac{1}{n}\right) = \log_e\left(1 + \frac{1}{n}\right)^n,$$

$$1 < (n+1) \log_e\left(1 + \frac{1}{n}\right) = \log_e\left(1 + \frac{1}{n}\right)^{n+1}.$$

From the inequalities

$$\log_e\left(1 + \frac{1}{n}\right)^n < 1 < \log_e\left(1 + \frac{1}{n}\right)^{n+1}$$

it follows that

$$\left(1 + \frac{1}{n}\right)^n < e < \left(1 + \frac{1}{n}\right)^{n+1}.$$

These last inequalities make it possible to evaluate e with any desired degree of accuracy: it is only necessary to introduce into the last inequalities a sufficiently large value of n. For instance, if $n = 100$, we obtain

$$2.703 < \left(1 + \frac{1}{100}\right)^{100} < e < \left(1 + \frac{1}{100}\right)^{101} < 2.732.$$

From this we see that

$$e \approx 2.7.$$

As $n \to \infty$, the fraction $\dfrac{1}{n} \to 0$ and

$$\frac{\left(1 + \dfrac{1}{n}\right)^{n+1}}{\left(1 + \dfrac{1}{n}\right)^{n}} = 1 + \frac{1}{n}$$

approaches 1; hence, as $n \to \infty$,

$$\left(1 + \frac{1}{n}\right)^{n} \quad \text{and} \quad \left(1 + \frac{1}{n}\right)^{n+1}$$

have the same limit. Then from the inequality

$$\left(1 + \frac{1}{n}\right)^{n} < e < \left(1 + \frac{1}{n}\right)^{n+1}$$

it follows that

$$e = \lim_{n \to \infty} \left(1 + \frac{1}{n}\right)^{n}. \tag{*}$$

This formula is often used as a definition of the number e.

Let us note also that formula (*) can be generalized as follows:

$$\lim_{n \to \infty} \left(1 + \frac{a}{n}\right)^{n} = e^{a}. \tag{**}$$

The proof of formula (**) is almost identical with the proof of formula (*). Let us suppose that in Fig. 36, $OP = 1 + \dfrac{a}{n}$, where $a > 0$. In that case we have

$$S_{K\dot{P}MA} = \log_{e}\left(1 + \frac{a}{n}\right),$$

$$S_{KP\overline{M}A} = KA \cdot KP = 1 \cdot \frac{a}{n} = \frac{a}{n},$$

$$S_{KPM\overline{A}} = KP \cdot PM = \frac{a}{n} \cdot \frac{1}{1 + \dfrac{a}{n}} = \frac{a}{n} \cdot \frac{n}{n+a} = \frac{a}{n+a}.$$

Therefore,

$$\frac{a}{n} > \log_{e}\left(1 + \frac{a}{n}\right) > \frac{a}{n+a}.$$

Moreover, in exactly the same manner as before, we obtain

$$a > n \log_e \left(1 + \frac{a}{n} \right) = \log_e \left(1 + \frac{a}{n} \right)^n,$$

$$a < (n + a) \log_e \left(1 + \frac{a}{n} \right) = \log_e \left(1 + \frac{a}{n} \right)^{n+a},$$

that is,

$$\log_e \left(1 + \frac{a}{n} \right)^n < a < \log_e \left(1 + \frac{a}{n} \right)^{n+a}$$

or, equivalently,

$$\left(1 + \frac{a}{n} \right)^n < e^a < \left(1 + \frac{a}{n} \right)^{n+a}.$$

As before we see that

$$\frac{\left(1 + \dfrac{a}{n} \right)^{n+a}}{\left(1 + \dfrac{a}{n} \right)^n} = \left(1 + \frac{a}{n} \right)^a$$

approaches 1 as $n \to \infty$. Hence,

$$\lim_{n \to \infty} \left(1 + \frac{a}{n} \right)^n = \lim_{n \to \infty} \left(1 + \frac{a}{n} \right)^{n+a};$$

formula (**) follows immediately.

In a completely analogous manner it is possible to prove that formula (**) also holds for negative values of a. In Fig. 36 let $OQ = 1 - \frac{a}{n}$, where $a > 0$. Then

$$S_{QKAN} = \log_e \frac{OK}{OQ} = \log_e \frac{1}{1 - \dfrac{a}{n}} = -\log_e \left(1 - \frac{a}{n} \right),$$

$$S_{QK\bar{A}N} = QK \cdot QN = \frac{a}{n} \cdot \frac{1}{1 - \dfrac{a}{n}} = \frac{a}{n - a},$$

$$S_{QKA\bar{N}} = KA \cdot QK = 1 \cdot \frac{a}{n} = \frac{a}{n}.$$

Therefore,

$$\frac{a}{n} < -\log_e \left(1 - \frac{a}{n} \right) < \frac{a}{n - a}.$$

In exactly the same manner as before, we obtain

$$a > -(n - a) \log_e \left(1 - \frac{a}{n}\right) = -\log_e \left(1 - \frac{a}{n}\right)^{n-a},$$

$$a < -n \log_e \left(1 - \frac{a}{n}\right) = -\log_e \left(1 - \frac{a}{n}\right)^{n}.$$

Hence,

$$-\log_e \left(1 - \frac{a}{n}\right)^{n-a} < a < -\log_e \left(1 - \frac{a}{n}\right)^{n}$$

or

$$\log_e \left(1 - \frac{a}{n}\right)^{n} < -a < \log_e \left(1 - \frac{a}{n}\right)^{n-a}$$

or, equivalently,

$$\left(1 - \frac{a}{n}\right)^{n} < e^{-a} < \left(1 - \frac{a}{n}\right)^{n-a}.$$

Exactly as before, it follows that

$$\lim_{n \to \infty} \left(1 - \frac{a}{n}\right)^{n} = e^{-a}.$$

In conclusion, let us derive a formula for the area of the curvilinear trapezoid $PQNM$ bounded by the hyperbola $xy = a$ $(a > 0)$, the x-axis, and the straight lines $x = x_1$, $x = x_2$ (Fig. 37). Let us

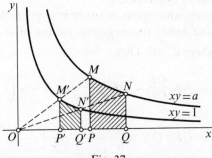

Fig. 37

apply a homothetic transformation with the origin as center and with coefficient $k = \dfrac{1}{\sqrt{a}}$. Under this transformation the hyperbola $xy = a$ will be transformed into the hyperbola $xy = 1$, a point with

40

coordinates (x, y) being transformed into the point with coordinates $\left(\dfrac{1}{\sqrt{a}}\,x, \dfrac{1}{\sqrt{a}}\,y\right)$. Hence, the curvilinear trapezoid $PQNM$ will be transformed into the curvilinear trapezoid $P'Q'N'M'$.

As we have seen,

$$S_{P'Q'N'M'} = \log_e\left(\frac{OQ'}{OP'}\right).$$

On the other hand, it follows from the properties of homothetic transformations (section 1) that

$$S_{P'Q'N'M'} = k^2 S_{PQNM} = \frac{1}{a}\,S_{PQNM},$$

and

$$\frac{OQ'}{OP'} = \frac{OQ}{OP} = \frac{x_2}{x_1}.$$

From this we obtain

$$S_{P'Q'N'M'} = \log_e\left(\frac{x_2}{x_1}\right),$$

$$S_{PQNM} = a \log_e\left(\frac{x_2}{x_1}\right).$$

In particular, if

$$a = \log_{10}e \approx 0.43,$$

the logarithm of the number e to the base 10, we obtain

$$S_{PQNM} = \log_{10}e \cdot \log_e\left(\frac{x_2}{x_1}\right).$$

Since $e = 10^{\log_{10}e}$, $z = e^{\log_e z} = (10^{\log_{10}e})^{\log_e z} = 10^{(\log_{10}e)(\log_e z)}$; from $z = 10^{\log_{10}z}$ it follows that

$$\log_{10}e \cdot \log_e z = \log_{10}z$$

and

$$S_{PQNM} = \log_{10}\left(\frac{x_2}{x_1}\right).$$

These remarks show that the logarithm of a number z to the base 10 can be defined as the area of the curvilinear trapezoid $KPMA$ bounded by the hyperbola $xy = \log_{10}e \approx 0.43$, the x-axis, and the straight lines $x = 1$, $x = z$; this is "the geometric definition" of logarithms to the base 10.

11. ANALYTIC EXPRESSIONS FOR THE HYPERBOLIC FUNCTIONS

We again consider the unit hyperbola $X^2 - Y^2 = 1$. Let M be an arbitrary point of that hyperbola, and let the hyperbolic angle AOM be equal to t. The coordinates of the points M and A relative to the coordinate system the axes of which coincide with the axes of the hyperbola are given by

$$OP = \cosh t, \; PM = \sinh t, \quad \text{and} \quad OA = 1, \; AA = 0.$$

The coordinates of these same points in the coordinate system the axes of which coincide with the asymptotes of the hyperbola are determined by the formulas in section 6 and are

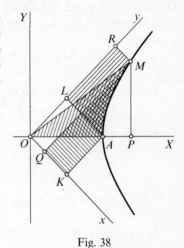

$$OQ = (\cosh t - \sinh t)\frac{\sqrt{2}}{2},$$

$$OR = (\cosh t + \sinh t)\frac{\sqrt{2}}{2};$$

$$OK = (1 - 0)\frac{\sqrt{2}}{2} = \frac{\sqrt{2}}{2},$$

$$OL = (1 + 0)\frac{\sqrt{2}}{2} = \frac{\sqrt{2}}{2}.$$

Fig. 38

Furthermore, it is easy to show that the areas of the curvilinear trapezoids $QKAM$ and $RLAM$ are equal and that each has the same area as the hyperbolic sector OAM. For, by the definition of the hyperbola (see p. 9), the areas of the coordinate rectangles of the points M and A are equal:

$$S_{OQMR} = S_{OKAL}.$$

It follows that

$$S_{QKAM} = S_{QKAM} - S_{OKAL} + S_{OQMR} = S_{RLAM}.$$

Also, since $S_{\triangle MOQ} = \frac{1}{2}S_{OQMR}$ and $S_{\triangle AOK} = \frac{1}{2}S_{OKAL}$,

$$S_{\triangle MOQ} = S_{\triangle AOK}.$$

From this we have

$$S_{QKAM} = S_{QKAM} - S_{\triangle AOK} + S_{\triangle MOQ} = S_{OAM}.$$

But by our definition of hyperbolic angles,

$$S_{OAM} = \frac{1}{2}t;$$

therefore,

$$S_{QKAM} = S_{RLAM} = \frac{1}{2}t.$$

Since the unit hyperbola has the equation $xy = \frac{1}{2}$ relative to the coordinate system the axes of which coincide with the asymptotes, it follows from the material at the end of the preceding section that

$$S_{QKAM} = \frac{1}{2}\log_e\left(\frac{OK}{OQ}\right)$$

$$= \frac{1}{2}\log_e \frac{\dfrac{\sqrt{2}}{2}}{(\cosh t - \sinh t)\dfrac{\sqrt{2}}{2}}$$

$$= -\frac{1}{2}\log_e(\cosh t - \sinh t),$$

and consequently,

$$\frac{1}{2}t = -\frac{1}{2}\log_e(\cosh t - \sinh t),$$

$$-t = \log_e(\cosh t - \sinh t). \qquad (*)$$

Analogously, we have

$$S_{RLAM} = \frac{1}{2}\log_e\left(\frac{OR}{OL}\right)$$

$$= \frac{1}{2}\log_e \frac{(\cosh t + \sinh t)\dfrac{\sqrt{2}}{2}}{\dfrac{\sqrt{2}}{2}}$$

$$= \frac{1}{2}\log_e(\cosh t + \sinh t),$$

from which we see that

$$\frac{1}{2}t = \frac{1}{2}\log_e(\cosh t + \sinh t),$$

$$t = \log_e(\cosh t + \sinh t). \qquad (**)$$

Formulas (*) and (**) establish a relationship between hyperbolic functions and logarithms to the base e. From these formulas we obtain

$$\cosh t - \sinh t = e^{-t},$$
$$\cosh t + \sinh t = e^t;$$

consequently,

$$\cosh t = \frac{e^t + e^{-t}}{2}, \tag{1}$$

$$\sinh t = \frac{e^t - e^{-t}}{2}. \tag{2}$$

Since (p. 24)

$$\tanh t = \frac{\sinh t}{\cosh t}, \tag{I}$$

we have

$$\tanh t = \frac{e^t - e^{-t}}{e^t + e^{-t}}. \tag{3}$$

Formulas (1)–(3) provide us with analytic expressions for the hyperbolic functions; they are often taken as the definitions of the hyperbolic functions in higher mathematics. From these three formulas we can easily derive all the identities which hold between the hyperbolic functions. Compare these derivations with those of Chapter 2.

First consider

$$\cosh^2 t - \sinh^2 t = \left(\frac{e^t + e^{-t}}{2}\right)^2 - \left(\frac{e^t - e^{-t}}{2}\right)^2$$

$$= \frac{e^{2t} + 2 + e^{-2t}}{4} - \frac{e^{2t} - 2 + e^{-2t}}{4} = 1;$$

hence,

$$\cosh^2 t - \sinh^2 t = 1. \tag{II}$$

Formulas (III) and (IV) can be derived similarly, and formulas (V)–(VII) can be derived by using the formulas for

$$\sinh t, \qquad \cosh t,$$
$$\sinh u, \qquad \cosh u.$$

Other examples follow:

$$2 \sinh t \cosh t = 2 \left(\frac{e^t - e^{-t}}{2} \right) \left(\frac{e^t + e^{-t}}{2} \right)$$

$$= \frac{(e^t - e^{-t})(e^t + e^{-t})}{2}$$

$$= \frac{e^{2t} - e^{-2t}}{2} = \sinh 2t;$$

hence,

$$2 \sinh t \cosh t = \sinh 2t. \qquad \text{(VIII)}$$

$$\cosh^2 t + \sinh^2 t = \left(\frac{e^t + e^{-t}}{2} \right)^2 + \left(\frac{e^t - e^{-t}}{2} \right)^2$$

$$= \frac{e^{2t} + 2 + e^{-2t}}{4} + \frac{e^{2t} - 2 + e^{-2t}}{4}$$

$$= \frac{e^{2t} + e^{-2t}}{2} = \cosh 2t;$$

hence,

$$\cosh^2 t + \sinh^2 t = \cosh 2t. \qquad \text{(IX)}$$

$$\frac{2 \tanh \frac{t}{2}}{1 - \tanh^2 \frac{t}{2}} = \frac{2 \dfrac{e^{\frac{t}{2}} - e^{-\frac{t}{2}}}{e^{\frac{t}{2}} + e^{-\frac{t}{2}}}}{1 - \left[\dfrac{e^{\frac{t}{2}} - e^{-\frac{t}{2}}}{e^{\frac{t}{2}} + e^{-\frac{t}{2}}} \right]^2}$$

$$= \frac{2 \left(e^{\frac{t}{2}} - e^{-\frac{t}{2}} \right) \left(e^{\frac{t}{2}} + e^{-\frac{t}{2}} \right)}{\left[\left(e^{\frac{t}{2}} + e^{-\frac{t}{2}} \right)^2 - \left(e^{\frac{t}{2}} - e^{-\frac{t}{2}} \right)^2 \right]}$$

$$= \frac{2 \left(e^{\frac{t}{2}} - e^{-\frac{t}{2}} \right) \left(e^{\frac{t}{2}} + e^{-\frac{t}{2}} \right)}{4} = \frac{e^t - e^{-t}}{2} = \sinh t;$$

hence,

$$\frac{2 \tanh \frac{t}{2}}{1 - \tanh^2 \frac{t}{2}} = \sinh t. \qquad \text{(XIV)}$$

It is possible to derive the other formulas similarly.

12. INFINITE SERIES EXPANSIONS FOR e^a, sinh t, cosh t

In order to obtain our final results from formulas (1) and (2), let us consider formula (**) of section 10.

By the binomial theorem we have

$$\left(1 + \frac{a}{n}\right)^n = 1 + \frac{n}{1} \cdot \frac{a}{n} + \frac{n(n-1)}{2!} \cdot \frac{a^2}{n^2} + \frac{n(n-1)(n-2)}{3!} \cdot \frac{a^3}{n^3} + \cdots$$

$$+ \frac{n(n-1)\cdots[n-(n-1)]}{n!} \cdot \frac{a^n}{n^n}$$

$$= 1 + \frac{a}{1} + \left(1 - \frac{1}{n}\right)\frac{a^2}{2!} + \left(1 - \frac{1}{n}\right)\left(1 - \frac{2}{n}\right)\frac{a^3}{3!} + \cdots$$

$$+ \left(1 - \frac{1}{n}\right)\left(1 - \frac{2}{n}\right)\cdots\left(1 - \frac{n-1}{n}\right)\frac{a^n}{n!}$$

$$= 1 + u_1 + u_2 + \cdots + u_n,$$

where

$$u_k = \left(1 - \frac{1}{n}\right)\left(1 - \frac{2}{n}\right)\cdots\left(1 - \frac{k-1}{n}\right)\frac{a^k}{k!} \qquad (k = 1, 2, \ldots, n).$$

In the sum

$$1 + u_1 + u_2 + \cdots + u_n$$

let us disregard all the terms $u_{k+1}, u_{k+2}, \ldots, u_n$ after a given term u_k. The error resulting from this will be

$$u_{k+1} + u_{k+2} + u_{k+3} + \cdots + u_n.$$

But from the definition of u_n, it follows that

$$|u_k| \leq \frac{|a|^k}{k!},$$

$$|u_{k+1}| = \left(1 - \frac{k}{n}\right)\frac{|a|}{k+1}|u_k| < \frac{|a|}{k+1}|u_k|,$$

$$|u_{k+2}| = \left(1 - \frac{k+1}{n}\right)\frac{|a|}{k+2}|u_{k+1}| < \frac{|a|}{k+1}|u_{k+1}| < \frac{|a|^2}{(k+1)^2}|u_k|,$$

$$|u_{k+3}| = \left(1 - \frac{k+2}{n}\right)\frac{|a|}{k+3}|u_{k+2}| < \frac{|a|}{k+1}|u_{k+2}| < \frac{|a|^3}{(k+1)^3}|u_k|,$$

and so on

($|a|$ denotes the absolute value of the number a).

Therefore, the sum

$$u_{k+1} + u_{k+2} + \cdots + u_n$$

does not exceed in absolute value the sum

$$|u_k|\frac{|a|}{k+1} + |u_k|\frac{|a|^2}{(k+1)^2} + |u_k|\frac{|a|^3}{(k+1)^3} + \cdots$$

$$+ |u_k|\frac{|a|^{n-k}}{(k+1)^{n-k}} = |u_k|\frac{\dfrac{|a|}{k+1} - \dfrac{|a|^{n-k+1}}{(k+1)^{n-k+1}}}{1 - \dfrac{|a|}{k+1}},$$

where we have made use of the fact that

$$|u_{k+1} + u_{k+2} + \cdots + u_n| \leq |u_{k+1}| + |u_{k+2}| + \cdots + |u_n|.$$

Let us now assume that

$$k + 1 > |a|.$$

(We assume that n is large enough for us to choose k in this manner.) Then the last expression is smaller than

$$|u_k|\frac{\dfrac{|a|}{k+1}}{1 - \dfrac{|a|}{k+1}} = |u_k|\frac{|a|}{k+1-|a|}$$

$$\leq \frac{|a|^k}{k!} \cdot \frac{|a|}{k+1-|a|}, \text{ since } u_k \leq \frac{|a|^k}{k!}.$$

In this way, replacing

$$\left(1 + \frac{a}{n}\right)^n$$

by the sum

$$1 + u_1 + u_2 + \cdots + u_k$$

will result in an error not greater in absolute value than

$$\frac{|a|^{k+1}}{k!\,(k+1-|a|)};$$

that is, for any n greater than k

$$\left|\left(1 + \frac{a}{n}\right)^n - (1 + u_1 + u_2 + \ldots + u_k)\right| < \frac{|a|^{k+1}}{k!\,(k+1-|a|)}.$$

Let us now consider this last expression as $n \to \infty$. Since

$$\lim_{n \to \infty} \left(1 + \frac{a}{n}\right)^n = e^a$$

(formula (**), section 10) and

$$u_1 = \frac{a}{1}, \quad \lim_{n \to \infty} u_2 = \frac{a^2}{2!}, \quad \lim_{n \to \infty} u_3 = \frac{a^3}{3!}, \quad \ldots, \quad \lim_{n \to \infty} u_k = \frac{a^k}{k!}$$

(see the formula defining u_k), we obtain

$$\left| e^a - \left(1 + a + \frac{a^2}{2!} + \frac{a^3}{3!} + \cdots + \frac{a^k}{k!}\right) \right| < \frac{|a|^{k+1}}{k! \, (k + 1 - |a|)}.$$

Let us now consider this expression as $k \to \infty$; we shall prove that

$$\lim_{k \to \infty} \frac{|a|^{k+1}}{k! \, (k + 1 - |a|)} = 0.$$

If we write, for short,

$$\frac{|a|^{k+1}}{k! \, (k + 1 - |a|)} = V_k,$$

we have

$$V_{k+l} = \frac{|a|^{k+l+1}}{(k + l)! \, (k + l + 1 - |a|.)}$$

$$= \frac{|a|^{k+1}}{k! \, (k + 1 - |a|)} \cdot \frac{k + 1 - |a|}{k + l + 1 - |a|} \cdot \frac{|a|^l}{(k + 1)(k + 2) \cdots (k + l)}$$

$$< V_k \cdot \frac{|a|^l}{(k + 1)^l} = V_k \alpha^l, \quad \text{where } \alpha = \frac{|a|}{k + 1}.$$

We have simply disregarded the factor

$$\frac{k + 1 - |a|}{k + l + 1 - |a|},$$

which is less than 1, while in the factor

$$\frac{|a|^l}{(k + 1)(k + 2) \cdots (k + l)}$$

we have replaced all the factors of the denominator by $(k + 1)$. But we have already assumed that $k + 1 > |a|$; therefore,

$$\frac{|a|}{k + 1} = \alpha < 1.$$

From the fact that $V_{k+l} < V_k \alpha^l$, and $\alpha < 1$, it follows that $V_{k+l} \to 0$ as $l \to \infty$, or

$$\lim_{k \to \infty} V_k = 0.$$

Finally, the inequality

$$\left| \left(1 + \frac{a}{n}\right)^n - \left(1 + a + \frac{a^2}{2!} + \frac{a^3}{3!} + \cdots \frac{a^k}{k!}\right) \right| < V_k$$

gives us

$$\lim_{k \to \infty} \left| e^a - \left(1 + a + \frac{a^2}{2!} + \frac{a^3}{3!} + \cdots + \frac{a_k}{k!}\right) \right| = 0$$

or

$$e^a = \lim_{k \to \infty} \left(1 + a + \frac{a^2}{2!} + \frac{a^3}{3!} + \cdots + \frac{a^k}{k!}\right).$$

Thus, e^a is equal to the sum of the infinite series

$$e^a = 1 + a + \frac{a^2}{2!} + \frac{a^3}{3!} + \cdots. \qquad (***)$$

This is the formula which we were trying to obtain.

Substituting into formula (***) first $a = t$ and then $a = -t$, we obtain

$$e^t = 1 + t + \frac{t^2}{2!} + \frac{t^3}{3!} + \frac{t^4}{4!} + \cdots,$$

$$e^{-t} = 1 - t + \frac{t^2}{2!} - \frac{t^3}{3!} + \frac{t^4}{4!} - \cdots.$$

Now, taking into account formulas (1) and (2), we obtain[1]

$$\cosh t = 1 + \frac{t^2}{2!} + \frac{t^4}{4!} + \frac{t^6}{6!} + \cdots, \qquad (4)$$

$$\sinh t = 1 + t + \frac{t^3}{3!} + \frac{t^5}{5!} + \cdots. \qquad (5)$$

Formulas (4) and (5) make it possible to calculate the values of $\sinh t$, $\cosh t$, and $\tanh t = \dfrac{\sinh t}{\cosh t}$ for any value of t with any desired degree of accuracy; we need only add up a sufficiently large number of terms of the corresponding infinite series. As a matter of fact, it is with the aid of these formulas that tables of hyperbolic functions are constructed.

[1] Operations with convergent series can be justified by calculus.

13. EULER'S FORMULAS

Expressions of the form b^a, where a is a real number, are often discussed in a second year high school algebra course. Usually no mention is made of expressions of the form 2^i or e^{2-4i}, where the exponent is not a real number. Using the formula

$$e^a = \lim_{n \to \infty} \left(1 + \frac{a}{n}\right)^n, \qquad (*)$$

which we have derived (section 10), we are in a position to define the expression e^a for any complex number a.

We shall first calculate $\lim\limits_{n \to \infty} \left(1 + \dfrac{a}{n}\right)^n$ for $a = \beta + i\alpha$, β and α being real numbers. Then

$$1 + \frac{a}{n} = \left(1 + \frac{\beta}{n}\right) + i\,\frac{\alpha}{n} = r_n(\cos\varphi_n + i\sin\varphi_n),$$

where

$$r_n = \sqrt{\left(1 + \frac{\beta}{n}\right)^2 + \left(\frac{\alpha}{n}\right)^2} = \sqrt{1 + \frac{2\beta}{n} + \frac{\alpha^2 + \beta^2}{n^2}},$$

and

$$\tan\varphi_n = \frac{\dfrac{\alpha}{n}}{1 + \dfrac{\beta}{n}}$$

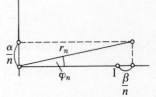

Fig. 39

(Fig. 39). From this we obtain

$$\left(1 + \frac{\alpha}{n}\right)^n = r_n{}^n(\cos\varphi_n + i\sin\varphi_n)^n.$$

But by DeMoivre's formula,

$$(\cos\varphi_n + i\sin\varphi_n)^n = \cos n\varphi_n + i\sin n\varphi_n,$$

and so

$$\left(1 + \frac{\alpha}{n}\right)^n = r_n{}^n(\cos n\varphi_n + i\sin n\varphi_n).$$

Therefore,

$$e^a = \lim_{n \to \infty}\left(1 + \frac{a}{n}\right)^n = R(\cos\Phi + i\sin\Phi),$$

where $R = \lim\limits_{n \to \infty}(r_n)^n,\quad \Phi = \lim\limits_{n \to \infty}(n\varphi_n).$

Let us now determine R. We have

$$R = \lim_{n\to\infty} \left(\sqrt{1 + \frac{2\beta}{n} + \frac{\alpha^2 + \beta^2}{n^2}} \right)^n.$$

Let us compare this expression with

$$e^\beta = \lim_{n\to\infty} \left(1 + \frac{\beta}{n} \right)^n = \lim_{n\to\infty} \left(\sqrt{\left(1 + \frac{\beta}{n}\right)^2} \right)^n$$

$$= \lim_{n\to\infty} \left(\sqrt{1 + \frac{2\beta}{n} + \frac{\beta^2}{n^2}} \right)^n$$

(see formula (*)). We have

$$\frac{R}{e^\beta} = \lim_{n\to\infty} \frac{\left(\sqrt{1 + \dfrac{2\beta}{n} + \dfrac{\beta^2 + \alpha^2}{n^2}} \right)^n}{\left(\sqrt{1 + \dfrac{2\beta}{n} + \dfrac{\beta^2}{n^2}} \right)^n}$$

$$= \lim_{n\to\infty} \left(\sqrt{\frac{1 + \dfrac{2\beta}{n} + \dfrac{\beta^2 + \alpha^2}{n^2}}{1 + \dfrac{2\beta}{n} + \dfrac{\beta^2}{n^2}}} \right)^n$$

$$= \lim_{n\to\infty} \left(\sqrt{1 + \frac{\dfrac{\alpha^2}{n^2}}{1 + \dfrac{2\beta}{n} + \dfrac{\beta^2}{n^2}}} \right)^n.$$

But for $\beta \geq 0$ and sufficiently large values of n, we have

$$1 \leq \left(1 + \frac{\beta}{n} \right)^2 < \left(1 + \frac{1}{2} \right)^2 = \frac{9}{4},$$

and, therefore,

$$\left(\sqrt{1 + \frac{\alpha^2}{n^2}} \right)^n \geq \left(\sqrt{1 + \frac{\dfrac{\alpha^2}{n^2}}{1 + \dfrac{2\beta}{n} + \dfrac{\beta^2}{n^2}}} \right)^n$$

$$= \left(\sqrt{1 + \frac{\dfrac{\alpha^2}{n^2}}{\left(1 + \dfrac{\beta}{n}\right)^2}} \right)^n > \left(\sqrt{1 + \frac{4\alpha^2}{9n^2}} \right)^n. \quad \text{(a)}$$

51

Thus, we must evaluate the following limits:

$$\lim_{n\to\infty} \left(\sqrt{1 + \frac{\alpha^2}{n^2}} \right)^n = \lim_{n\to\infty} \left(1 + \frac{\alpha^2}{n^2} \right)^{\frac{n}{2}}$$

$$= \lim_{n\to\infty} \left[\left(1 + \frac{\alpha^2}{n^2} \right)^{n^2} \right]^{\frac{1}{2n}}.$$

and

$$\lim_{n\to\infty} \left(\sqrt{1 + \frac{4\alpha^2}{9n^2}} \right)^n = \lim_{n\to\infty} \left[\left(1 + \frac{4\alpha^2}{9n^2} \right)^{n^2} \right]^{\frac{1}{2n}}$$

Let us now make use of the fact that for large values of n we have as a result of formula (*)

$$\left(1 + \frac{\alpha^2}{n^2} \right)^{n^2} \approx e^{\alpha^2} \quad \text{and} \quad \left(1 + \frac{4\alpha^2}{9n^2} \right)^{n^2} \approx e^{\frac{4\alpha^2}{9}}.$$

And since

$$\lim_{n\to\infty} (e^{\alpha^2})^{\frac{1}{2n}} = 1 \quad \text{and} \quad \lim_{n\to\infty} (e^{\frac{4\alpha^2}{9}})^{\frac{1}{2n}} = 1,[1]$$

both the limits in question must be equal to 1.

If $\beta < 0$, then, for sufficiently large values of n,

$$1 \geq \left(1 + \frac{\beta}{n} \right)^2 > \left(1 - \frac{1}{2} \right)^2 = \frac{1}{4},$$

and in the formula analogous to formula (a) the inequality signs must be reversed. The rest of the proof remains as before.

Thus, for any value of β

$$\lim_{n\to\infty} \left(\sqrt{1 + \frac{\dfrac{\alpha^2}{n^2}}{1 + \dfrac{2\beta}{n} + \dfrac{\beta^2}{n^2}}} \right)^n = 1;$$

and, therefore,

$$\frac{R}{e^\beta} = 1, \quad R = e^\beta.$$

---

[1] This follows, for instance, from the fact that for any number a

$$\lim_{n\to\infty} [\log a^{\frac{1}{2n}}] = \lim_{n\to\infty} \frac{\log a}{2n} \to 0,$$

from which it follows that

$$\lim_{n\to\infty} a^{\frac{1}{2n}} = 1.$$

Let us now determine Φ. We have

$$\Phi = \lim_{n \to \infty}(n\varphi_n) = \lim_{n \to \infty}\left(\frac{\varphi_n}{\tan\varphi_n} \cdot n\tan\varphi_n\right)$$

$$= \lim_{n \to \infty}\left(\frac{\varphi_n}{\tan\varphi_n} \cdot \frac{\alpha}{1 + \dfrac{\beta}{n}}\right).$$

But since $\tan\varphi_n = \dfrac{\dfrac{\alpha}{n}}{1 + \dfrac{\beta}{n}} \to 0$ as $n \to \infty$, we have

$$\varphi_n \to 0 \text{ as } n \to \infty.$$

Therefore,

$$\lim_{n \to \infty}\frac{\varphi_n}{\tan\varphi_n} = \lim_{\varphi \to 0}\frac{\varphi}{\tan\varphi} = \lim_{\varphi \to \infty}\frac{\varphi}{\sin\varphi} \cdot \cos\varphi,$$

Since $\lim\limits_{\varphi \to 0}\cos\varphi = 1$ and $\lim\limits_{\varphi \to 0}\dfrac{\varphi}{\sin\varphi} = 1$,[1] we have

$$\lim_{n \to \infty}\frac{\varphi_n}{\tan\varphi_n} = \lim_{\varphi \to 0}\frac{\varphi}{\sin\varphi} \cdot \cos\varphi = 1.$$

Moreover, since $\lim\limits_{n \to \infty}\dfrac{\alpha}{1 + \dfrac{\beta}{n}} = \alpha$, it follows that

$$\Phi = \lim_{n \to \infty}\left(\frac{\varphi_n}{\tan\varphi_n} \cdot \frac{\alpha}{1 + \dfrac{\beta}{n}}\right) = \alpha.$$

Thus, $R = e^\beta$, $\Phi = \alpha$, and consequently,

$$e^{\beta + i\alpha} = e^\beta(\cos\alpha + i\sin\alpha). \tag{**}$$

Now we can be certain that our definition of e^a is satisfactory. In fact, this definition fulfills two basic requirements, which could have been set forth beforehand:

1. For each *real* number a, the definition of e^a given in (**) yields the same result as the ordinary definition (since for real numbers $\alpha = 0$, $\cos\alpha = 1$, $\sin\alpha = 0$).

[1] Proved in calculus.

53

2. The numbers e^a thus defined satisfy the following fundamental rule for multiplication:

$$e^{a_1} \cdot e^{a_2} = e^{a_1 + a_2}.$$

For, if $a_1 = \beta_1 + i\alpha_1$ and $a_2 = \beta_2 + i\alpha_2$, we have

$$e^{a_1} \cdot e^{a_2} = e^{\beta_1 + i\alpha_1} \cdot e^{\beta_2 + i\alpha_2}$$

$$= e^{\beta_1} (\cos \alpha_1 + i \sin \alpha_1) \cdot e^{\beta_2} (\cos \alpha_2 + i \sin \alpha_2)$$

$$= e^{\beta_1} \cdot e^{\beta_2} (\cos \alpha_1 + i \sin \alpha_1)(\cos \alpha_2 + i \sin \alpha_2)$$

$$= e^{\beta_1 + \beta_2} [\cos (\alpha_1 + \alpha_2) + i \sin (\alpha_1 + \alpha_2)]$$

$$= e^{\beta_1 + \beta_2 + i(\alpha_1 + \alpha_2)} = e^{a_1 + a_2}.$$

Now let us substitute first $i\alpha$, and then $-i\alpha$, for a in the expression (**) on page 53. We then obtain

$$e^{i\alpha} = \cos \alpha + i \sin \alpha,$$

$$e^{-i\alpha} = \cos (-\alpha) + i \sin (-\alpha) = \cos \alpha - i \sin \alpha.$$

From these two formulas it follows immediately that

$$\cos \alpha = \frac{e^{i\alpha} + e^{-i\alpha}}{2}, \qquad (1')$$

$$\sin \alpha = \frac{e^{i\alpha} - e^{-i\alpha}}{2i}; \qquad (2')$$

therefore, since $\tan \alpha = \dfrac{\sin \alpha}{\cos \alpha}$, we have

$$\tan \alpha = \frac{e^{i\alpha} - e^{-i\alpha}}{i \, (e^{i\alpha} + e^{-i\alpha})}. \qquad (3')$$

These are Euler's formulas which establish the relationship between trigonometric functions and exponential functions.[1]

From formulas (1') and (2') it is possible to obtain further results. In fact, let us substitute for a in formula (***) on page 49, first $i\alpha$, and then $-i\alpha$.[2] We then obtain

$$e^{i\alpha} = 1 + i\alpha - \frac{\alpha^2}{2!} - \frac{i\alpha^3}{3!} + \frac{\alpha^4}{4!} + \frac{i\alpha^5}{5!} - \frac{\alpha^6}{6!} - \cdots,$$

$$e^{-i\alpha} = 1 - i\alpha - \frac{\alpha^2}{2!} + \frac{i\alpha^3}{3!} + \frac{\alpha^4}{4!} - \frac{i\alpha^5}{5!} - \frac{\alpha^6}{6!} + \cdots.$$

[1] Leonhard Euler (1707–1783), a great 18th-century mathematician.

[2] The derivation of formula (***) of section 12 from formula (**) of section 10 is completely valid even for complex values of a. (Only here the vertical bars must be taken to denote the modulus of the complex number, that is, the square root of the sum of the squares of the real part of the number and the coefficient of i.)

Taking into account (1') and (2') we obtain

$$\cos \alpha = 1 - \frac{\alpha^2}{2!} + \frac{\alpha^4}{4!} - \frac{\alpha^6}{6!} + \cdots, \tag{4'}$$

$$\sin \alpha = \alpha - \frac{\alpha^3}{3!} + \frac{\alpha^5}{5!} - \frac{\alpha^7}{7!} + \cdots. \tag{5'}$$

Formulas (4') and (5') make it possible to calculate the values of $\sin \alpha$, $\cos \alpha$, and $\tan \alpha = \dfrac{\sin \alpha}{\cos \alpha}$ for any value of α with any given degree of accuracy; we need only add up a sufficiently large number of terms of the corresponding infinite series. As a matter of fact, it is with the aid of these formulas that tables of trigonometric functions are constructed.